GREAT MINDS® WIT & WISDOM™

Grade 6 Module 2:
A Hero's Journey

Student Edition

COPYRIGHT STATEMENT

Published by Great Minds®.

ISBN: 978-1-68386-042-6

Table of Contents

Name

Date Class

Handout 1A: Sanjay's Super Team

Part I Directions: As you watch the animated short film by Sanjay Patel, "Sanjay's Super Team," record what you notice and wonder.

I Notice	I Wonder

Part 2 Directions: Review your notice/wonder notes in light of what you learned in today's lesson and compose a Quick Write explaining what connections you see, what you now understand about *Ramayana's* context, characters, and/or history as well as what questions you have.

Name

Date Class

Handout 1B: Frayer Model

Directions: Write the given word in the middle, then complete the surrounding boxes.

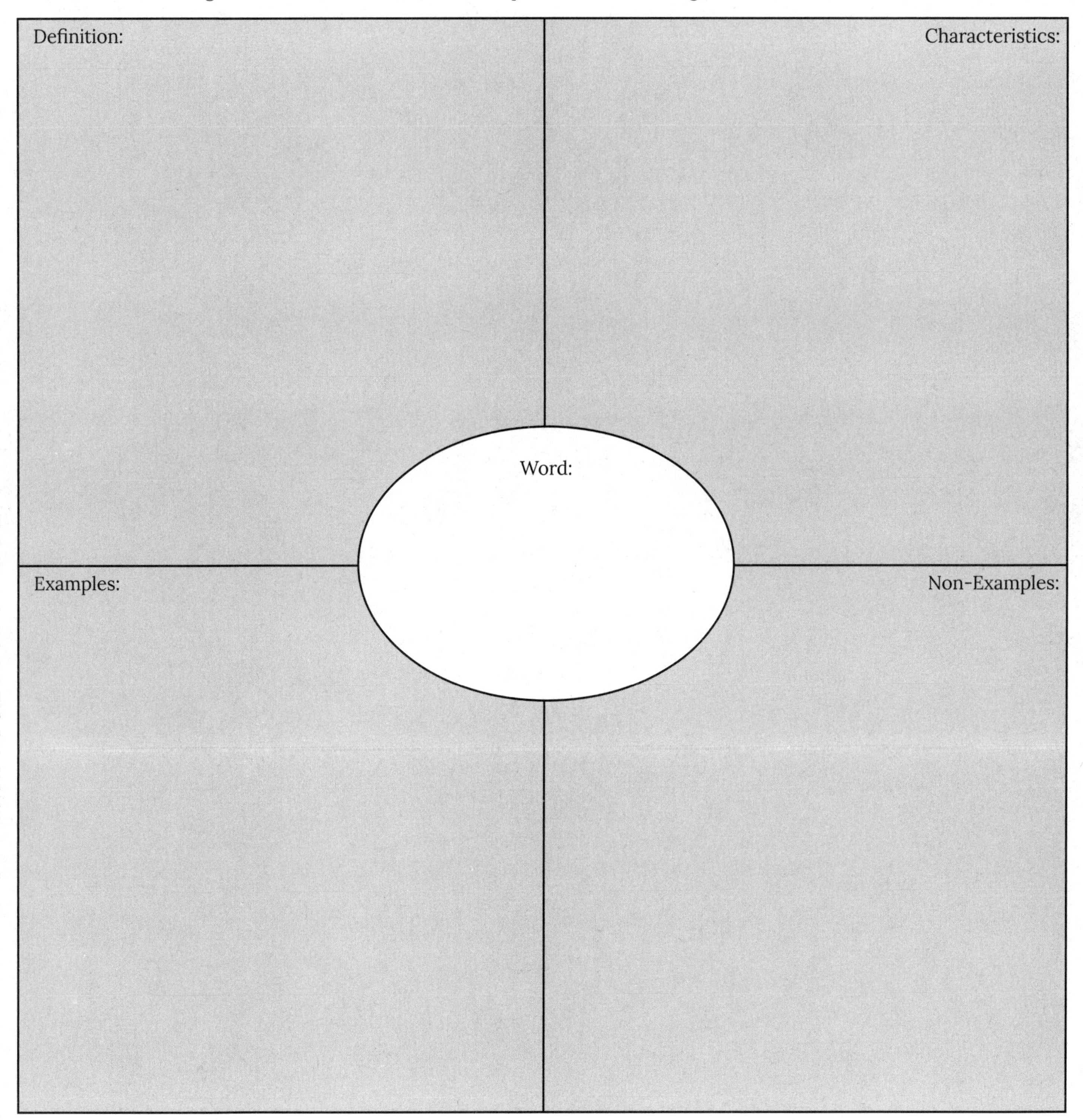

Name

Date Class

Handout 2A: Anticipation Guide

Directions: For each of the following statements, please indicate whether you agree or disagree and then briefly explain your opinion. Consider what your personal experiences have taught you and/or what you have seen on the news or in movies or read in newspapers, magazines, and books.

Agree	Disagree	Statement	Explanation
		1. It is important to choose to do what is right rather than what is easy.	
		2. The old maxim is true: what goes around, comes around.	
		3. Children have a duty to follow their parents' wishes and commands, even if they disagree with them.	
		4. It is important always to keep your word; you should never break a promise.	
		5. Most heroes are exceptional people with extraordinary abilities.	
		6. Heroes always need help and assistance if they are to be successful.	
		7. A person only becomes a hero through struggle.	

Name

Date Class

Handout 2B: Group Word-Solving Process

Directions: With your group, complete the process on the given word.

WORD:	
1. Check if any group members know the word already.	
2. Check "outside" the word to see whether there are any clues in the text around it.	
3. Check "inside" the word to see whether there are clues from the root or affix.	
4. Check a reference, such as a thesaurus or dictionary.	
5. Check back in the text to confirm the meaning in the dictionary makes sense to the context.	

Name

Date Class

Handout 2C: Word Solving

Directions: Use the Group Word-Solving Process (Handout 2B) to determine the meaning of the words in bold. Write the definitions on the line.

***cosm* = "world or universe"** **_serv_ = "to keep or save"**

1. His winning strategy was to **conserve** his energy until the very last lap of the race.

2. I will **reserve** judgment until I know more about the situation.

3. The aquarium is like a **microcosm** of the ocean.

4. To celebrate their anniversary, the couple made a **reservation** at their favorite restaurant.

5. Though it is small, the city attracts immigrants from all over the world and has quite a **cosmopolitan** feeling.

Name

Date Class

Handout 3A: Act One Sequence

Part I Directions: Review the chapters from Act One in *Ramayana: Divine Loophole* and add any missing minor or major plot points to the myth's sequence of events below.

Number	Event Sequence
1	Ravana meditates for thousands of years and almost kills himself in the hopes that the gods will grant him his wish to be "the most powerful creature in the universe" (14).
2	
3	Ravana releases the demons from the "lowest level of hell," dethrones Indra, and destabilizes the universe (17).
4	
5	Rama is born as a prince in the capital city of Ayodhya.
6	
7	Rama and his brother Lakshman are additionally trained by the sage Vishvamitra. He gives both brothers "profound strength and mental focus" (24).
8	
9	Vishvamitra takes Rama to a neighboring kingdom, and the prince completes the test of lifting Shiva's bow.
10	Rama is given Sita as a reward.
11	
12	
13	
14	
15	Sita and Lakshman follow Rama into exile.
16	
17	Bharata returns after hearing the news of his father's death and learns that Rama has been exiled.
18	
19	Bharata places Rama's shoes on the throne and refuses to become king.
20	Bharata and Shatrughna begin their own exile out of respect for Rama.

Name

Date Class

Part II Directions: Working with a partner, take ten minutes to respond to the following TDQs. Use Handout 3A, your Response Journals, and the text as needed to support your answers.

1. Which plot points establish a context for Rama's hero's journey? Why are these plot points logical to include at the beginning of this story?

2. Which plot point begins Rama's story? What experiences and events define Rama's early youth?

3. Which major plot point changes the direction of the story and shakes up the status quo? Locate a quotation that states this new direction for the story.

4. (*if time allows*) Which events make sense, or are logical, because of the role *dharma* plays in the characters' lives?

Name

Date Class

Handout 3B: Adjectives to Nouns

Directions: Fill in the blank spaces on the table by converting adjectives to nouns or nouns to adjectives. In the final four rows, come up with your own words to show in both adjective and noun forms.

Adjective	Noun
none	integrity
hostile	hostility
	vulnerability
capable	
eternal	
	charity
curious	
serene	
	sanity
sensitive	

Name

Date Class

Handout 4A: Chapter Analysis

Directions: Working with your group, analyze your assigned chapter by responding to the following questions in your Response Journals.

Group 1: "Forest Dwellers" (40–41)
Group 2: "Hermit Handouts" (42–45)
Group 3: "Fatal Attraction" (46–47)
Group 4: "Nosey Demon" (48–51)
Group 5: "Divine Arrow" (52–53)

1. **Where/When** (setting): Where does this scene take place? When does this scene take place and how long of a time frame does it span?

2. **Who** (characters): Who are the main characters in this chapter and what do they want? For characters who have been introduced prior to this scene, what more do we learn about each of them from this chapter? For new characters, what do we learn about each of their traits and their relationships to the other characters?

3. **What/How** (action/plot): What happens in this chapter and how do the characters respond? What are the minor plot points that move the story forward? What are any major plot points that upset the balance of things and head the larger story in a new direction?

4. **Why** (sequence): Why is this scene happening? What events from past chapters have created the need for this scene? How does this chapter help to develop the myth's plot?

5. How do the chapter's accompanying **illustrations** support or expand on what is being depicted in the chapter?

Name

Date Class

Handout 4B: Narrative Practice

Directions: Follow the steps below to complete the first of several assignments to help you practice different aspects of narrative writing so that you can gradually write a narrative scene.

Step 1: Choose Your Character

Choose and read one of the following character profiles from *Ramayana: Divine Loophole*. You will use the information in this profile as the seed of a narrative scene that you will begin to create.

- King Dasaratha (134–35)
- Tataka (160)
- Kaikeyi (138–39)

Step 2: Create Your Scene Outline

Review the annotated Elements of a Narrative (Handout 4C), and fill in what you can on the blank organizer (also part of Handout 4C) using the content provided by Patel in his profile. Then, using your imagination and your knowledge of the story so far, create the content for as many of the rest of the narrative elements as you can. Remember: you may use your imagination to make your scene vivid and engaging, but you must stay true to the character(s) and the event(s) the text summarizes. Below is a sample using Vishvamitra's profile (130).

Vishvamitra			
Beginning	E	Establish	
	S	Setting	Thousands of years ago in a faraway Indian kingdom.
	C	Characters	Vishvamitra is not yet a rishi, but instead is a "war-faring king" who is obsessed with power (130). He "curses and kills many to rise to the throne," not caring who he hurts as long as he selfishly gets something out of it (130).
Middle	A	Action	(1) While hunting with his other lords, Vishvamitra spots a cow that casts off a golden light, and he tries to shoot it (130). (2) The cow disappears, and in its place, a man emerges who holds his hands in prayer. (3) Vishvamitra threatens to kill him if he does not produce the golden cow. (4) The man introduces himself as the guru Vasishta, and with a nod of his head, removes all the weapons and armor from Vishvamitra and his men. (5) Vasishta informs Vishvamitra that his selfish ways must end, for true power is not acquired by taking it from others, but by giving it away in the form of service. Vasishta magically rips open his chest, and the image of Vishnu gazes fiercely at Vishvamitra. (6) Vishvamitra falls to his knees and thanks the guru for helping him gain awareness.
	P	Problem	Vishvamitra loves power. He does not want to change his ways. However, due to his interaction with Vasishta, he recognizes that he needs to change because his behavior and desires are evil.
End	E	Ending	Vishvamitra "sees the error of his ways and retreats from society to perform penance" (130). He becomes a rishi because he transforms from being evil to being wise.

Name

Date Class

Step 4: Draft Opening Paragraph (Context)
Using what you have learned from Patel about establishing context, draft the opening paragraph of your scene. You can write below or in your Response Journal. This paragraph does not need to be lengthy, but it should provide enough information about the setting, main characters, and plot so that a reader feels oriented to the scene and wants to read more. Below is a sample for Vishvamitra.

> *Thousands of years ago in a faraway Indian kingdom, there lived a war-faring king named Vishvamitra who was obsessed with power. He cursed and killed many to rise to the throne, not caring who he hurt as long as he selfishly got something out of it. His greatest pleasure was hunting the magnificent beasts in the jungle near his castle, and he took pride in his collection of mounted heads, each one an awesome display of his power.*

Reminder: Keep and reference this handout and Handout 4C as you continue writing this scene in the upcoming lessons.

Name

Date Class

Handout 4C: Narrative Writing Graphic Organizer

The Elements of a Narrative: ESCAPE into a Scene!			
Beginning	**E**	Establish	How does the author open the scene, by engaging the reader and establishing a context and point of view?
	S	Setting	**When** and **where** does this chapter's scene take place?
	C	Characters	**Who** is featured in the chapter's scene and what do they want?
Middle	**A**	Action	**What** events happen and **how** do the characters experience these events? *Note: many of the scene's events will be minor plot points that move the plot forward. One or two might be major plot points that change the direction of the larger story beyond this scene.* **Why** is this scene happening? What events from past chapters have created the need for this scene? How does this chapter help to develop the myth's plot?
	P	Problem	What is the **conflict** the character(s) faces in this scene or what prevents the character(s) from getting what he/she wants?
End	**E**	Ending	What is the **resolution** to the problem or conflict in this scene or how does the scene end?

Name

Date Class

The Elements of a Narrative: ESCAPE into a Scene!			
Beginning	E	Establish	
	S	Setting	
	C	Characters	
Middle	A	Action	
	P	Problem	
End	E	Ending	

Name

Date Class

Handout 5A: Speaking and Listening Checklist

Directions: Complete the following to set and track your goals and progress toward effective speaking and listening during our discussion. See next page for Socratic Seminar sentence-starters to help you during discussion.

1. Before we begin our discussion, what is your goal for today's Socratic Seminar to improve your participation?

2. After our discussion, complete the checklist below.

Grade 6 Speaking and Listening Checklist			
	Self +/ Δ	Peer +/ Δ	Teacher +/ Δ
I used text evidence to support my opinion.			
I asked questions.			
I followed all the rules for speaking in a group.			
I set and met my participation goal.			
I built and elaborated on comments from my peers.			
I agreed and disagreed respectfully and strategically.			
▪ I used a polite tone of voice throughout the discussion.			
▪ I used my knowledge of why people disagree to resolve disagreements.			
I deferred politely to other speakers.			
▪ I listened respectfully to the ideas of others.			
▪ I helped others get a chance to speak.			
I stayed engaged in the conversation the whole time.			
I brought the conversation back on topic when needed.			

Name

Date Class

3. Did you meet the goal you set for today? Why or why not?

4. What might be your goal for our next discussion? Why?

Name

Date Class

Socratic Seminar Sentence Starters

Statements and Questions	For Clarification or Paraphrasing
▪ I wonder why... ▪ What if we looked at this in a different way, such as... ▪ What in the text makes you say that? ▪ How does that support our idea about... ▪ In my mind I see... ▪ Based on..., I infer that... ▪ Do you agree or disagree with... ▪ I am still confused by... ▪ Based on..., I predict that...	▪ Could you please rephrase that? ▪ Can you say more about that? ▪ I have a question about that... ▪ Could someone please paraphrase that? ▪ In other words, are you saying...?
For Building Ideas	**For Different Viewpoint**
▪ I agree with...and I'd like to add... ▪ I really like that idea because... ▪ That idea is important because... ▪ If we change that a little, we can see... ▪ Another example of... is... ▪ This reminds me of... ▪ Now I am wondering... ▪ This relates back to our essential question because...	▪ That's a great point, but I think... ▪ I agree with the part about..., but I think... ▪ On the other hand, what about... ▪ The evidence seems to suggest something different, such as... ▪ I politely disagree with...because...
Partners	**Problem-Solving**
▪ We decided that... ▪ During the Turn-and-Talk, _______ pointed out to me that... ▪ After our Think-Pair-Share, I believe I have a new idea... ▪ We concluded that...	▪ I think the way to continue is... ▪ We should identify... ▪ I think we should do this step-by-step starting with... ▪ Another way to look at this is... ▪ I feel like we are missing something because... ▪ Maybe we can reframe this by... ▪ Which thinking map could we use to help us?
Summarizing	**Other**
▪ I'd like to go back to what... was saying and... ▪ So, the big idea is... ▪ So, what can we conclude from this? ▪ After our analysis, it appears that... ▪ Several things contributed to this conclusion. The most important was...	▪ ▪ ▪ ▪ ▪ ▪ ▪

Name

Date Class

Handout 5B: Optional Fluency Practice 1

Directions:

1. Day 1: Read the text carefully and annotate to help you read fluently.
2. Each day:
   a. Practice reading the text three to five times.
   b. Evaluate your progress by placing a √+, √, or √- in each unshaded box.
   c. Ask someone (adult or peer) to listen and evaluate you as well.
3. Last day: Respond to the self-reflection questions.

The demonic deer grinned, oozing blood from its mouth, and told Rama that today he would atone for his previous crimes. The prince had no idea what the demon was talking about, which was no surprise to the demon, since Maricha knew that the prince had forgotten taking the life of his mother, Tataka, while training with the brahmarshi. Maricha had waited for years for this day and finally felt he was on the verge of avenging his mother's death. With its last breath, the demonic deer told Rama that now it was his time to face his karma and then cried out for help, imitating Rama's voice perfectly. Instantly, the blue prince realized he had made a grave mistake. (Patel 61)

Student Performance Checklist:	Day 1		Day 2		Day 3		Day 4	
	You	Listener*	You	Listener*	You	Listener*	You	Listener*
Accurately read the passage 3–5 times.								
Read with appropriate phrasing and pausing.								
Read with appropriate expression.								
Read articulately at a good pace and an audible volume.								

*Adult or peer

Name

Date Class

Self-reflection: What choices did you make when deciding how to read this passage, and why? What would you like to improve on or try differently next time? (*Thoughtfully answer these questions below.*)

Name

Date Class

Handout 5C: Pronoun Case

Directions: Fill in each of the blanks in the table with the correct corresponding subjective, objective, or possessive pronoun. Use the sentences frames below to help you in determining the correct pronoun case.

- Sentence with missing **subjective** pronoun: ____ *threw the ball.*
- Sentence with missing **objective** pronoun: *The ball hit* _____.
- Sentence with missing **possessive** pronoun: *That is* _____ *ball.*

Subjective	Objective	Possessive
I	me	my
	us	
		your
he		
	her	
it		
		their

Name

Date Class

Handout 6A: Precise Word Choice and Illustrations

Directions: With your group, complete the following on chart paper for the main character featured in your assigned chapter. When done, post your chart for the Gallery Walk.

Chapter: **Character:**	
1. What **precise words and phrases** develop this character? *Consider all parts of speech when searching for precise words: adjectives, adverbs, nouns, and verbs.*	What does this use of language convey about character?
2. What **specific details** from the **illustrations** develop this character?	What does this use of image convey about character?
3. What is the impact of the author depicting the characters in this way? In other words, how do these depictions help advance the plot, convey a theme, or develop another character?	

Name

Date Class

Handout 8A: "The Hero's Journey Outline"

Directions: The following are Christopher Vogler's stages, which are a simplified version of Joseph Campbell's 1949 original concepts. Refer to these throughout this module as needed.

The Hero's Journey is a pattern of narrative identified by the American scholar Joseph Campbell that appears in drama, storytelling, myth, religious ritual, and psychological development. It describes the typical adventure of the archetype known as The Hero, the person who goes out and achieves great deeds on behalf of the group, tribe, or civilization. It's stages are:

Stage	Description
PHASE 1 – THE DEPARTURE	
1. The Ordinary World	The hero, uneasy, uncomfortable or unaware, is introduced sympathetically so the audience can identify with the situation or dilemma. The hero is shown against a background of environment, heredity, and personal history. Some kind of polarity in the hero's life is pulling in different directions and causing stress.
2. The Call to Adventure	Something shakes up the situation, either from external pressures or from something rising up from deep within, so the hero must face the beginnings of change.
3. Refusal of the Call	The hero feels the fear of the unknown and tries to turn away from the adventure, however briefly. Alternately,another character may express the uncertainty and danger ahead.
4. Meeting with the Mentor	The hero comes across a seasoned traveler of the worlds who gives him or her training, equipment, or advice that will help on the journey. Or the heroreaches within to a source of courage and wisdom.
5.Crossing the Threshold	At the end of Act One, the hero commits to leaving the Ordinary World and entering a new region or condition with unfamiliar rules and values.
PHASE 2 – THE INITIATION	
6. Test, Allies, and Enemies	The hero is tested and sorts out allegiances in the Special World.
7. Approach	The hero and newfound allies prepare for the major challenge in the Special World.
8. The Ordeal	Near the middle of the story, the hero enters a central space in the Special World and confronts death or faces his or her greatest fear. Out of the moment of death comes a new life.
9. The Reward	The hero takes possession of the treasure won by facing death. There may be celebration, but there is also danger of losing the treasure again.
PHASE 3 – THE RETURN	
10. The Road Back	About three-fourths of the way through the story, the hero is driven to complete the adventure, leaving the Special World to be sure the treasure is brought home. Often a chase scene signals the urgency and danger of the mission.
11. The Resurrection	At the climax, the hero is severely tested once more on the threshold of home. He or she is purified by a last sacrifice, another moment of death and rebirth, but on a higher and more complete level. By the hero's action, the polarities that were in conflict at the beginning are finally resolved.
12. Return with the Elixir	The hero returns home or continues the journey, bearing some element of the treasure that has the power to transform the world as the hero has been transformed.

From Vogler, Christopher. "The Hero's Journey Outline." Storytech Literary Consulting. Storytech, 1985. Web. 1 July 2016. Vogler, Christopher. The Writer's Journey: Mythic Structure for Writers. 3rd Edition. Studio City, CA: Michael Wiese Productions, 2007.

Name

Date Class

Handout 8B: Viv/Vit Word Web

Directions: Follow the step-by-step verbal directions provided by your teacher to complete this organizer.

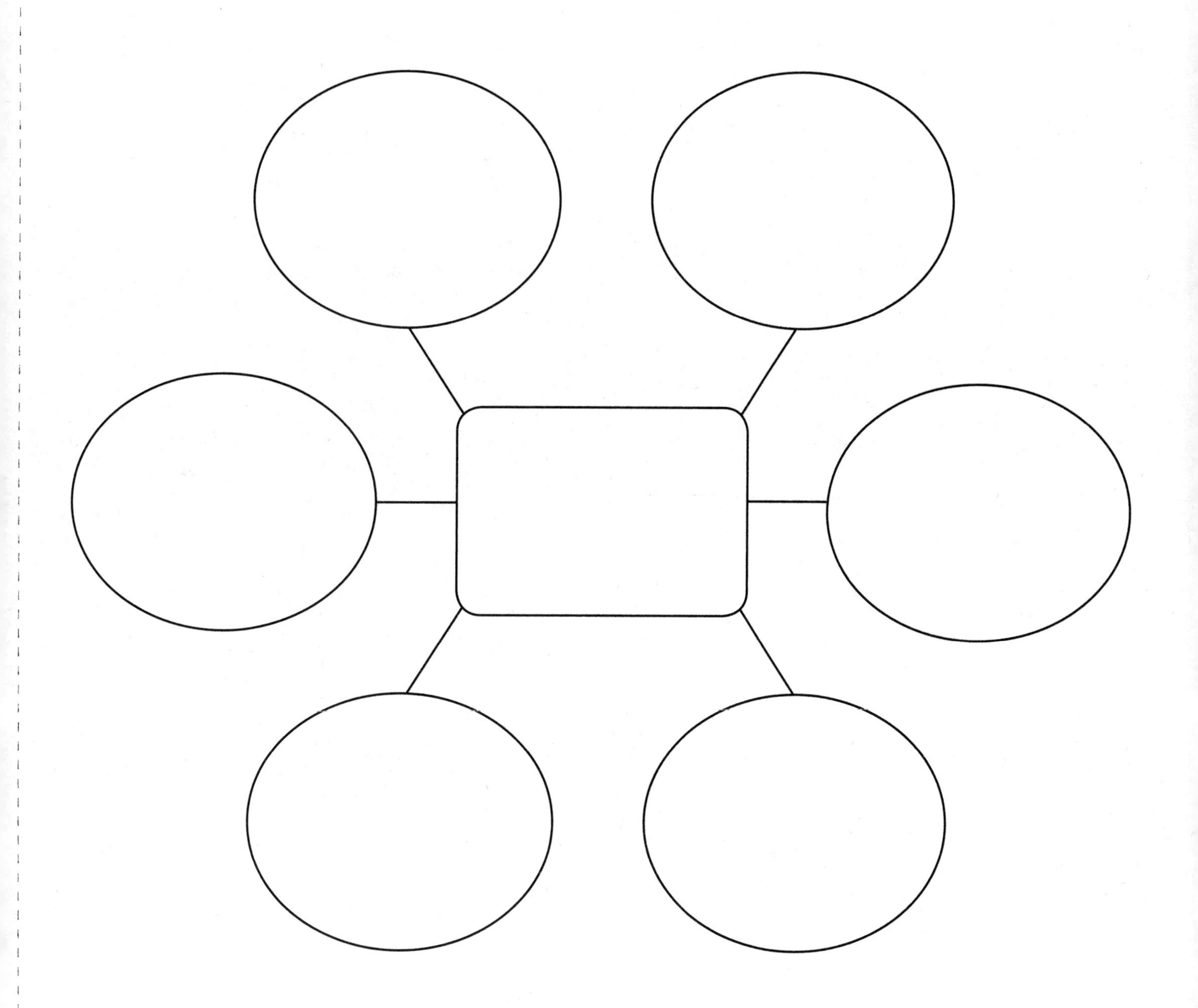

Name

Date Class

Handout 9A: Character Archetypes

Directions: Add the title of the text in the top row of the table and then for each of the character archetypes explain who or what fills that role in the text under study and how he/she/they/it exhibits that archetype's characteristics. If an archetype is not present in the text, write N/A for that archetype's row.

Character Archetypes in ______	
Archetype	**Character Details**
Hero	
Shadow	
Mentor	
Ally	
Threshold Guardians	
Herald	
Shapeshifter	

Name ______________________

Date ______________ Class ______________

Handout 9B: Stages of a Hero's Journey

Directions: Add the title of the text in the top row of the table and then complete the columns for each stage of the hero's journey that is present in the text under study. If a stage is not present, write N/A in both columns for that stage's row.

Stages of a Hero's Journey in ______________		
Vogler's Stage	**What occurs during this stage in this text?**	**How do the events of this stage help develop this text's themes?**
PHASE 1 – THE DEPARTURE		
1. The Ordinary World		
2. Call to Adventure		
3. Refusal of the Call		
4. Meeting with the Mentor		

Name ______________________

Date ____________ Class ____________

Vogler's Stage	What occurs during this stage in this text?	How do the events of this stage help develop this text's themes?
5. Crossing the Threshold		
PHASE 2 – THE INITIATION		
6. Tests, Allies, and Enemies		
7. Approach		
8. The Ordeal		
9. The Reward		

Name

Date Class

Vogler's Stage	What occurs during this stage in this text?	How do the events of this stage help develop this text's themes?
PHASE 3 – THE RETURN		
10. The Road Back		
11. The Resurrection		
12. Return with the Elixir		

Name

Date Class

Handout 9C: Explanatory Essay Graphic Organizers

Directions: You may use these optional graphic organizers to help you plan your explanatory essay.

Introduction
Hook
Introduce
Thesis and Preview

Name

Date Class

Body Paragraph 1 Organizer	
Topic Statement:	
Evidence: Citation:	**E**laboration:
Evidence: Citation:	**E**laboration:
Concluding Statement:	

Name

Date Class

Body Paragraph 2 Organizer	
Topic Statement:	
Evidence: Citation:	**E**laboration:
Evidence: Citation:	**E**laboration:
Concluding Statement:	

Name

Date Class

Conclusion

Name

Date Class

Handout 10A: Anticipation Guide

Directions: For each of the following statements, please indicate whether you agree or disagree and then briefly explain your opinion. Consider what your personal experiences have taught you and/or what you have seen on the news or in movies or read in newspapers, magazines, and books.

Agree	Disagree	Statement	Explanation
		1. It is a person's duty to keep his/her word, never break promises, never shirk responsibilities.	
		2. Self-control is overrated; a person should give in to temptation if it brings him/her pleasure.	
		3. Leaders are responsible for the actions of their followers.	
		4. Intelligence is more important for a warrior to possess than strength.	
		5. A person should be as proud as he/she wants of his/her accomplishments. There is no such thing as excessive pride.	
		6. Failure and struggle are necessary for a person to become great.	
		7. Fate or destiny controls a person's life more so than free will.	

Name

Date Class

Handout 10B: Optional Fluency Practice 2

Directions:

1. Day 1: Read the text carefully and annotate to help you read fluently.
2. Each day:
   a. Practice reading the text three to five times.
   b. Evaluate your progress by placing a √+, √, or √- in each unshaded box.
   c. Ask someone (adult or peer) to listen and evaluate you as well.
3. Last day: Respond to the self-reflection questions.

Out of the mysterious past comes this tale of human endurance, full of unknown dangers and terrifying monsters. It tells the adventures of a man who spent ten years fighting the anger of the raging sea as he struggled to sail home.

This is the story of Odysseus of Ithaca, cleverest of all the kings of ancient Greece. (Cross 9)

Student Performance Checklist:	Day 1		Day 2		Day 3		Day 4	
	You	Listener*	You	Listener*	You	Listener*	You	Listener*
Accurately read the passage 3–5 times.								
Read with appropriate phrasing and pausing.								
Read with appropriate expression.								
Read articulately at a good pace and an audible volume.								

*Adult or peer

Self-reflection: What choices did you make when deciding how to read this passage, and why? What would you like to improve on or try differently next time? (*Thoughtfully answer these questions on the back of this paper.*)

Name ______________________

Date ____________ Class ____________

Handout 10C: Word Lines

Directions: As a group, choose and circle one of the following word pairs. Then, follow the directions in steps 1–4.

wits - cunning ally - comrade

1. Write four synonyms of the chosen words.

______________________ ______________________

______________________ ______________________

2. Discuss the connotations of each word, using the denotations (dictionary definitions) as a guide.

3. Create a Word Line that displays the words in order of intensity. Write the agreed-upon order in the blanks below.

____________, ____________, ____________, ____________, ____________, ____________

4. Be prepared to justify your decisions!

Name

Date Class

Handout 11A: Sequence of Events

Part I Directions: Review the first three chapters from *The Odyssey* and add any missing minor or major plot points to the myth's sequence of events below.

Number	Event Sequence
1	Paris of Troy runs off with Helen the queen of Sparta and starts a war. Odysseus reluctantly joins the other Greek kings in battle.
2	Odysseus fights in Troy for ten years, and the Greeks ultimately defeat the Trojans through trickery. Odysseus and his men begin their journey home.
3	
4	The Cicones attack and kill many of Odysseus's men. Odysseus and some of the men escape.
5	
6	They land on an unknown shore, and Odysseus sends three men to see if they can find food and water.
7	
8	Odysseus's men do not want to return to the ships, but Odysseus orders that the drugged men be forcibly carried off and brought back to the ships.
9	They set sail again, and later land on another unknown shore. It is an island, and the men rest and feast.
10	Odysseus notices that across on the mainland there is noise and smoke from fires. Odysseus leaves eleven of the ships moored at the island, and takes his own ship and crew over to the mainland to explore.
11	
12	The Cyclops arrives and finds the men in his cave. Odysseus tries to explain that they come in peace, but the Cyclops grabs two of Odysseus's men and eats them.
13	
14	When the Cyclops returns, he eats more of Odysseus's men. Odysseus offers the Cyclops strong wine, which the monster drinks, and Odysseus tells him his name: Noe Boddy. The Cyclops tells Odysseus he, too, has a gift: he will eat Odysseus last. Then he passes out.
15	
16	The Cyclops is determined to not let the men escape. He sits at the front of his cave.
17	

Name

Date Class

18	The men race toward their ship and escape. However, when they set sail, Odysseus makes the mistake of "yelling triumphantly" at the Cyclops back on shore that Odysseus, king of Ithaca, has defeated him (44).
19	The Cyclops becomes enraged and begs his father, the god Poseidon, to put a curse on Odysseus.
20	

Part II Directions: Working with a partner, take ten minutes to respond to the following TDQs. Use your Response Journals and the text as needed to support your answers.

1. Which events establish a context for Odysseus's hero's journey? Why are these events logical to include? What phase of the hero's journey do they represent?

2. For the rest of Handout 11A's sequence of events, what phase and stage of the hero's journey do they represent? Why?

3. What is important about the last event in the sequence?

Name

Date Class

Handout 11B: Context Clues

Part I Directions: Read each passage from *The Odyssey*. Circle the words that help you understand the meaning of the word in bold. On the lines, write the characteristics or mood of the characters in the scene, and your guess of the bolded word's meaning.

1. Through the fog, a dark mass of land loomed ahead of them, but they were too exhausted to think of exploring it. They had just enough energy to **stagger** up the beach, out of range of the tide. (Cross 25)

Characteristics or mood of the men

What might **staggered** mean?

2. As soon as he began to snore, Odysseus **darted** forward, ready to draw his sword. (Cross 36)

Characteristics or mood of Odysseus

What might **darted** mean?

3. The Cyclops milked his sheep and **swilled** down two bucketfuls of milk. Then he grabbed two sailors for his supper, crunching their bones as he chewed them up. (Cross 38)

Characteristics or mood of the Cyclops

What might **swilled** mean?

Name ______________________________

Date ______________ Class ______________

4. The Cyclops rolled his eye and **bellowed** with laughter.
"Here it is. I promise to eat all your companions before I eat you. Isn't that a fine gift?" (Cross 38–39)

Characteristics or mood of the Cyclops

____

What might **bellowed** mean?

____

5. As soon as he was unconscious, Odysseus ran to the back of cave to fetch the pole he had sharpened. Once again, he and his men **plunged** it into the fire. But this time they held it there until it was red-hot. (Cross 39)

Characteristics or mood of Odysseus

____

What might **plunged** mean?

____

Name

Date Class

Handout 13A: Odysseus's Tests

Directions: Complete the table for your group's assigned section of the text.

Section	What is the test in this section?	What enables Odysseus to pass the test?	How is failure or disappointment part of this test?	What lesson does Odysseus learn?	What big ideas does this test convey?
The Lotus Eaters (21–25)	Odysseus and his men are tempted to eat the lotus fruit.	Odysseus is fiercely loyal to his family. He reminds the drugged men about their wives and families. His loyalty to family helps him pass the test of temptation.	Odysseus's men disappoint him when they taste the lotus fruit and become entranced; they are not as self-controlled as he needs them to be. They no longer want to return home since they are drugged. They give in to temptation, and they encourage the others to join them. Their actions almost destroy their chances of returning home.	Odysseus's men, although warriors, are flawed. Odysseus witnesses their weakness and understands how powerful temptation is. He warns the other men of its danger: "Don't even lick the juice from your fingers" (Cross 24). This test teaches him that the urge to give up is a weakness in all men. If he is to return home, he needs to stay focused on his end goal and persevere.	Temptation causes men to behave in ways that are self-destructive. Temptation must be resisted. Self-control is important.
The Cyclops (31–45)					

Name

Date Class

Section	What is the test in this section?	What enables Odysseus to pass the test?	How is failure or disappointment part of this test?	What lesson does Odysseus learn?	What big ideas does this test convey?
Aeolus and the bag (52–55)					
The Laestrygonians (58–62)					
Circe (64–72)					

Name

Date Class

Section	What is the test in this section?	What enables Odysseus to pass the test?	How is failure or disappointment part of this test?	What lesson does Odysseus learn?	What big ideas does this test convey?
The Underworld (76–80)					
The Sirens (81–85)					
Scylla and Charybdis (87–90)					

Name

Date Class

Section	What is the test in this section?	What enables Odysseus to pass the test?	How is failure or disappointment part of this test?	What lesson does Odysseus learn?	What big ideas does this test convey?
The island of Thrinacia (91–96)					
Encounter with Zeus and reencounter with Scylla and Charybdis (96–98)					

Name

Date Class

Handout 13B: Pronoun Case Passage

Part I Directions: Circle the pronouns in the excerpt below. Then, for each circled pronoun, determine if the one used is correct; if it is not, then cross it out and write in the correct pronoun. Finally, label each pronoun with an S (subjective), O (objective), or P (possessive) to indicate its case.

Odysseus is much more patient than his men. While them are tempted by various things along the way, he does not follow their path. The men and him are determined to get to Ithaca, but there are differences between he and them. He stays focused on the goal—reuniting with his wife. He will do anything to reach she and his son. He keeps them in his thoughts throughout the long journey.

Name

Date Class

Handout 14A: Narrative Techniques

Directions: Use this handout as needed when writing narratives.

Technique	Explanation
Dialogue	Helps the reader achieve better understanding of the characters; builds and releases tension; moves the plot forward.
Inner monologue	Unspoken thoughts by a character that help the reader achieve better understanding of that character; builds and releases tension; moves the plot forward.
Narration	Within a scene, helps connect dialogue between characters; provides description of characters' thoughts and actions that occur because of dialogue and inner monologue; moves the plot forward.
Pacing	Controls the speed at which a scene's sequence of events unfolds; can involve a combination of dialogue, inner monologue, and narration.
Description	Slows the story down so that important details can be highlighted.
Sentence variation	Emphasizes certain moments; creates interest; slows or speeds up the unfolding of a scene's events.

Name

Date Class

Handout 15A: Plot Analysis

Directions: Complete the table for your group's assigned event in the chapter "Nausicaa," using the completed row from an earlier chapter as a model. Use evidence from the text in your response and provide explanation. Record your answer on a chart that can be displayed for a Gallery Walk.

Event	How does this event advance the story?	How does this event help develop the hero, shadow, and/or mentor archetype?	What big idea is conveyed by this event in the plot?	How does this event fit into the structure of the hero's journey?
*Odysseus becomes trapped on Calypso's island, and Athene becomes involved on his behalf. (100–102, 106–7) **This model event is taken from the chapter "Stranded on Calypso's Island."*	Odysseus has not been able to leave the island because the goddess Calypso has "fallen in love with him" (100). In this scene, Hermes orders Calypso to release Odysseus, and she grudgingly obeys.	Odysseus is "wretched" and feels hopeless, for he does not see how he can think or fight his way out of this situation (100). His cunning and strength cannot defeat an enemy like Calypso, for she is a goddess. The hero needs a mentor, which Athene represents, for she operates behind the scene and pressures Zeus to order Calypso to free Odysseus.	Struggling can humble a person and bring rewards. Odysseus is made aware of the little power he has in controlling his fate. He knows that "all he [can] do [is] dream of going home" (102). Being trapped on Calypso's island with no means of escape humbles Odysseus. This humility impresses Athene, and she rewards his noble suffering by becoming involved in his fate.	The Approach Odysseus is still being tested and has not yet faced the shadow archetype. However, as emphasized in the illustration on page 109, he has no more men to lose and is on his own; he is approaching some sort of final test. At this point in his journey, Odysseus cannot return home without the help of a mentor, and now Athene has become involved. Her involvement will help Odysseus begin his return home, cycling back to Ithaca where his journey began.

Name

Date Class

Event	How does this event advance the story?	How does this event help develop the hero, shadow, and/or mentor archetype?	What big idea is conveyed by this event in the plot?	How does this event fit into the structure of the hero's journey?
Odysseus meets Nausicaa and accepts her help. (123–25)				
Odysseus journeys to the palace and meets Queen Arete and King Alcinous. (126–27)				

Name

Date Class

Event	How does this event advance the story?	How does this event help develop the hero, shadow, and/or mentor archetype?	What big idea is conveyed by this event in the plot?	How does this event fit into the structure of the hero's journey?
Odysseus attends the feasts and celebration hosted by King Alcinous. (127–31)				
Poseidon rages over Odysseus's return. (136)				

Name

Date Class

Handout 15B: Optional Fluency Practice 3

Directions:

1. Day 1: Read the text carefully and annotate to help you read fluently.
2. Each day:
   a. Practice reading the text three to five times.
   b. Evaluate your progress by placing a √+, √, or √- in each unshaded box.
   c. Ask someone (adult or peer) to listen and evaluate you as well.
3. Last day: Respond to the self-reflection questions.

"What mockery is this?" he bellowed at Zeus. "I have left this vile man wrecked and destitute–and the Phaeacians have made him rich. I shall destroy their ship and drown their sailors! And I'll fling up a circle of huge mountains around their city to cut it off from the rest of the world. Let them learn to fear me!" (Cross 136)

Student Performance Checklist:	Day 1		Day 2		Day 3		Day 4	
	You	Listener*	You	Listener*	You	Listener*	You	Listener*
Accurately read the passage 3–5 times.								
Read with appropriate phrasing and pausing.								
Read with appropriate expression.								
Read articulately at a good pace and an audible volume.								

*Adult or peer

Self-reflection: What choices did you make when deciding how to read this passage, and why? What would you like to improve on or try differently next time? (*Thoughtfully answer these questions on the back of this paper.*)

Name

Date Class

Handout 19A: Art Vocabulary

Directions: This reference explains some art vocabulary that we used in Module 1 and that we will be using in this module to discuss the illustrations in *Ramayana: Divine Loophole* and *The Odyssey*, as well as later modules. Keep this handout in your Vocabulary Journal and refer to it as needed to support your learning.

background (n.) - The area in a picture that seems to be the farthest away.

balance (n.) - A way of organizing the shapes and colors in a work of art so that the sides appear even. The three types of balance are symmetrical, asymmetrical, and radial.

color (n.) - The way we see light reflected from objects. Red, blue, and yellow are colors.

complementary colors (n. pl.) - Colors that are opposite each other on the color wheel - red/green, blue/orange, and yellow/violet.

composition (n.) - How an artist organizes the components in a work of art.

contrast (n.) – When an artist puts things that look different next to each other. Artists can contrast two or more colors, textures, lines, or shapes.

figure (n.) - A human or animal in a work of art.

focal point (n.) - The part of a work of art that seems most important.

foreground (n.) - The part of a painting, photograph, or drawing that seems closest to the viewer.

line (n.) - A mark made by drawing with a pencil or paintbrush. Line is one of the elements of art.

pattern (n.) - A regular, repeated design. Pattern is a principle of art.

pose (n.) – How a figure is standing or sitting in a work of art.

realistic (adj.) – Showing something the way it might look "in real life."

shape (n.) - An area bounded by a line.

geometric shape (n.) – A shape with even sides, curves, or edges such as a circle, square, or triangle.

organic shape (n.) – A shape that seems to come from nature, with uneven edges and sides.

silhouette (n.) - A dark form or shape against a lighter background.

symmetry (n.) – When each side of a work of art has similar but opposite shapes, similar to butterfly wings.

Name

Date Class

Handout 19B: Illustration Analysis

Directions: Working with your small group, complete the table below for your assigned illustration, using Handout 19A and your own inferences. Record information for at least four of the art elements. Then, individually respond to the question 7.

Illustration:		
Art element	**Describe this element in the illustration.**	**What does this aspect of the illustration reveal about the characters, setting, or event?**
1. Pose		
2. Line		
3. Color		

Name ______________________

Date ____________ Class ____________

Art element	Describe this element in the illustration.	What does this aspect of the illustration reveal about the characters, setting, or event?
4. Shape		
5. Background		
6.		

7. Describe one way in which analyzing illustrations helped you better understand this text.

Name

Date Class

Handout 19C: Hero Development

Directions: Use the questions below to help you create your original hero for your monomyth.

What is your hero's name? How would you describe your hero? (optional: sketch your character)	What does your hero want?
	What are your hero's strengths?

Name

Date Class

What is your hero's flaw or weakness?	
How will your hero overcome this flaw?	
What will your hero do to make life better for all people?	
In what ways will your hero grow into a wiser, better person after the journey?	

Name

Date Class

Handout 20A: Context Development

Directions: Use the questions below to help you create the context for your hero's journey.

How would you describe your hero's ordinary world?	How would you describe the unknown world into which your hero must venture?	What problem does your hero's flaw create in the unknown world?
What is the conflict in your myth? (Hint: What does your hero want and what does he/she have to do to get it?)	**How does this conflict force your hero to overcome his or her flaw?**	**How does the resolution of this conflict make life better for all people?**

Name

Date Class

Handout 21A: Listening and Reading–*The Odyssey*

Directions: Follow the directions for each step below.

1. Create a larger version of the following table on a sheet of paper or in your Response Journal as directed by your teacher.

	Listening	Reading
What do I "hear"?		
What do I "see"?		
What do I wonder?		

2. Listen to actor Ian McKellen read an excerpt of Fagles's translation from "Book 23" ("Penelope's Disbelief"), and complete the "Listening" column in the table.

3. Read the text of the same excerpt of Fagles's translation from "Book 23" (page 1 of Handout 21B), and complete the "Reading" column in the table.

Name

Date Class

Handout 21B: Translations of Homer's *Odyssey*

Directions: Please follow the directions on Handout 21A for the first translation of "Penelope's Disbelief." Then turn to the next page for directions about the homework with the remaining translations contained in this handout.

"Ἀλκίνοε κρεῖον, πάντων ἀριδείκετε λαῶν,
ἦ τοι μὲν τόδε καλὸν ἀκουέμεν ἐστὶν ἀοιδοῦ
τοιοῦδ' οἷος ὅδ' ἐστί, θεοῖς ἐναλίγκιος αὐδήν.
οὐ γὰρ ἐγώ γέ τί φημι τέλος χαριέστερον εἶναι
ἢ ὅτ' εὐφροσύνη μὲν ἔχῃ κάτα δῆμον ἅπαντα,
δαιτυμόνες δ' ἀνὰ δώματ' ἀκουάζωνται ἀοιδοῦ
ἥμενοι ἑξείης, παρὰ δὲ πλήθωσι τράπεζαι
σίτου καὶ κρειῶν, μέθυ δ' ἐκ κρητῆρος ἀφύσσων
οἰνοχόος φορέῃσι καὶ ἐγχείῃ δεπάεσσι·
τοῦτό τί μοι κάλλιστον ἐνὶ φρεσὶν εἴδεται εἶναι.
σοὶ δ' ἐμὰ κήδεα θυμὸς ἐπετράπετο στονόεντα
εἴρεσθ', ὄφρ' ἔτι μᾶλλον ὀδυρόμενος στεναχίζω·
τί πρῶτόν τοι ἔπειτα, τί δ' ὑστάτιον καταλέξω;
κήδε' ἐπεί μοι πολλὰ δόσαν θεοὶ Οὐρανίωνες.
νῦν δ' ὄνομα πρῶτον μυθήσομαι, ὄφρα καὶ ὑμεῖς
εἴδετ', ἐγὼ δ' ἂν ἔπειτα φυγὼν ὕπο νηλεὲς ἦμαρ
ὑμῖν ξεῖνος ἔω καὶ ἀπόπροθι δώματα ναίων.

Homer. "Book 9." *The Odyssey*. Trans. Geoffrey Steadman. Dec. 2012. Web. 1 July 2016.

Penelope's Disbelief	
The old nurse ran to Penelope's room and leaned over her bed. "Wake up!" she said. "Your prayers have all been answered. Odysseus is here!" Penelope lifted her head from the pillow. "Don't make fun of me," she said. "I'm serious," Eurycleia insisted. "That old beggar was Odysseus in disguise. And now he's destroyed all your wicked suitors. Come and see." Penelope still didn't believe her. "How could one man on his own defeat so many people? If the suitors have really been killed, it must have been done by one of the gods. Odysseus died long ago, in some far-off foreign land." "What nonsense!" Eurycleia said, "Come downstairs and you'll see." (Cross 166)	
1996 (verse)	
Up to the rooms the old nurse clambered, chuckling all the way, to tell the queen her husband was here now, home at last. Her knees bustling, feet shuffling over each other, till hovering at her mistress's head she spoke: "Penelope–child–wake up and see for yourself, with your own eyes, all you dreamed of, all your days! He's here–Odysseus–he's come home, at long last! He's killed the suitors, swaggering young brutes who plagued his house, wolfed his cattle down, rode roughshod over his son!" "Dear old nurse," wary Penelope replied, "the gods have made you mad. They have that power, putting lunacy into the clearest head around or setting a half-wit on the path to sense. They've unhinged you, and you were once so sane. Why do you mock me?–haven't I wept enough?– telling such wild stories, interrupting my sleep, sweet sleep that held me, sealed my eyes just now. Not once have I slept so soundly since the day Odysseus sailed away to see that cursed city ... Destroy, I call it–I hate to say its name!	Now down you go. Back to your own quarters. If any other woman of mine had come to me, rousing me out of sleep with such a tale, I'd have her bundled back to her room in pain. It's only your old gray head that spares you that!" "Never"–the fond old nurse kept pressing on– "dear child, I'd never mock you! No, it's all true, he's here–Odysseus–he's come home, just as I tell you! He's the stranger they all manhandled in the hall. Telemachus knew he was here, for days and days, but he knew enough to hide his father's plans so he could pay those vipers back in kind!" Penelope's heart burst in joy, she leapt from bed, her eyes streaming tears, she hugged the old nurse and cried out with an eager, winging word, "Please, dear one, give me the whole story. If he's really home again, just as you tell me, how did he get those shameless suitors in his clutches?– single-handed, braving an army always camped inside." (Fagles 380–81)

Name

Date Class

Homework Directions: Choose three of the additional five translations of "Penelope's Disbelief" provided on this and the next page to read and annotate; make sure you do a mix of prose (#1, #2, #3) and verse (#4, #5) translations. Then read and annotate all of the "Reconciliation" translations on the last page.

Penelope's Disbelief		
The old nurse ran to Penelope's room and leaned over her bed. "Wake up!" she said. "Your prayers have all been answered. Odysseus is here!" Penelope lifted her head from the pillow. "Don't make fun of me," she said. "I'm serious," Eurycleia insisted. "That old beggar was Odysseus in disguise. And now he's destroyed all your wicked suitors. Come and see." Penelope still didn't believe her. "How could one man on his own defeat so many people? If the suitors have really been killed, it must have been done by one of the gods. Odysseus died long ago, in some far-off foreign land." "What nonsense!" Eurycleia said. "Come downstairs and you'll see." (Cross 166)		
#1: 1891 (prose)	**#2: 1900 (prose)**	**#3: 1932 (prose)**
So the old woman, full of glee, went to the upper chamber to tell her mistress her dear lord was in the house. Her knees grew strong; her feet outran themselves. By Penelope's head she paused and thus she spoke: "Awake, Penelope, dear child, to see with your own eye what you have hoped to see this many a day Odysseus is here! He has come home at last, and slain the haughty suitors, – the men who vexed this house, devoured his substance, and oppressed his son." Then heedful Penelope said to her: "Dear nurse, the gods have crazed you/ They can befool one who is very wise, and often they have confused you; you were sober-minded heretofore. Why mock me when my heart is full of sorrow, telling wild tales like these? And why arouse me from the sleep that sweetly bound me and kept my eyelids closed? I have not slept so soundly since Odysseus went away to see accursed Ilios, –name never to be named. Nay then, go down back to the hall. If any other of my maids had come and told me this and waked me out of sleep, I would soon have sent her off in sorry wise into the hall once more. This time ago serves you well." Then said to her the good nurse Eurycleia: "Dear child, I do not mock you. In very truth it is Odysseus; he is come, as I have said. He is the stranger whom everybody in the hall has set at naught. Telemachus knew long ago that he was here, but out of prudence hid his knowledge of his father till he should have revenge from these bold men for wicked deeds. So she spoke; and Penelope was glad, and springing from her bed, fell on the woman's neck, and let tears burst from her eye; and, speaking in winged words, she said: "Nay, tell me, then, dear nurse, and tell me truly; if he is really come as you declare, how was it he laid hands upon the shameless suitors, being alone, while they were always here together? (Palmer 358–59)	Eurycleia now went upstairs laughing to tell her mistress that her dear husband had come home. Her aged knees became young again and her feet were nimble for joy as she went up to her mistress and bent over her head to speak to her. "Wake up Penelope, my dear child," she exclaimed, "and see with your own eyes something that you have been wanting this long time past. Ulysses has at last indeed come home again, and has killed the suitors who were giving so much trouble in his house, eating up his estate and ill treating his son." "My good nurse," answered Penelope, "you must be mad. The gods sometimes send some very sensible people out of their minds, and make foolish people become sensible. This is what they must have been doing to you; for you always used to be a reasonable person. Why should you thus mock me when I have trouble enough already–talking such nonsense, and waking me up out of a sweet sleep that had taken possession of my eyes and closed them? I have never slept so soundly from the day my poor husband went to that city with the ill-omened name. Go back again into the women's room; if it had been any one else who had woke me up to bring me such absurd news I should have sent her away with a severe scolding. As it is your age shall protect you." "My dear child," answered Euryclea, "I am not mocking you. It is quite true as I tell you that Ulysses is come home again. He was the stranger whom they all kept on treating so badly in the cloister. Telemachus knew all the time that he was come back, but kept his father's secret that he might have his revenge on all these wicked people." Then Penelope sprang up from her couch, threw her arms round Euryclea, and wept for joy. "But my dear nurse," said she, "explain this to me; if he has really come home as you say, how did he manage to overcome the wicked suitors single handed, seeing what a number of them there always were?" (Butler)	But it was with a cackle of laughter that the old dame climbed towards the upper room, to warn her mistress of the beloved husband's return. Her knees moved nimbly and her feet tripped along to the lady's bed-head where she stood and spoke her part. "Awake dear child, Penelope: open your eyes upon the sight you have yearned for all these days. Odysseus has appeared, at this end of time. He has reached his home and in it slaughtered the recalcitrant suitors who for so long vexed the house, ate his stored wealth and outfaced his son." Circumspect Penelope replied to this: "Dear mother, the Gods have driven you frantic. They turn to foolishness the ripest judgements and the flighty into sober ways. From them comes this derangement of your old true understanding: but why tease with fantasies a heart already brimmed with grief? Why wake me from this sleep whose sweetness held me in thrall and veiled my eyelids; the best sleep I have enjoyed since Odysseus went away to view that ill city never-to-be-named. Off with you below, instantly, to the women's quarters. Had any other of my house-maidens roused me with news of this sort I should have sent her smartingly back into her place. Just for this once your great age shall excuse you." Eurycleia persisted. "Dear child, I am in very earnest with you. Odysseus, I say, is here. He came back to the house as that stranger who met such scurvy treatment at all hands. Telemachus long since learnt his identity but very properly hid the knowledge, to let his father's revenge take shape against those proud rough men." This time her word transported Penelope who leaped from the couch and clasped the old woman, crying shrilly through the tears that rained from her eyes: "Ah, dear mother, but tell me, tell me truly–if as you say he is really come home, how has he coped single-handed with the shameless suitors, who mobbed our house continually?" (Lawrence)

Name

Date Class

Penelope's Disbelief (continued)	
#4: 1961 (verse)	#5: 2007 (verse)
The old nurse went upstairs exulting, with knees toiling, and patter of slapping feet, to tell the mistress of her lord's return, and cried out by the lady's pillow: "Wake, wake up, dear child! Penélopê, come down, see with your own eyes what all these years you longed for! Odysseus is here! Oh, in the end, he came! And he has killed your suitors, killed them all who made his house a bordelo and ate his cattle and raised their hands against his son!" Penélopê said: "Dear nurse . . . the gods have touched you. They can put chaos into the clearest head or bring a lunatic down to earth. Good sense you always had. They've touched you. What is this mockery you wake me up to tell me, breaking in on my sweet spell of sleep? I had not dozed away so tranquilly since my lord went to war, on that ill wind to Ilion. Oh, leave me! Back down stairs! If any other of my women came in babbling things like these to startle me, I'd see her flogged out of the house! Your old age spares you that." Eur´ykleia said: "Would I play such a trick on you, dear child? It is true, true, as I tell you, he has come! That stranger they were baiting was Odysseus. Telémakhos knew it days ago– cool head, never to give his father away, till he paid off those swollen dogs!" The lady in her heart's joy now sprang up with sudden dazzling tears, and hugged the old one, crying out: "But try to make it clear! If he came home in secret, as you say, could he engage them singlehanded? How? They were all down there, still in the same crowd." (Fitzgerald 570–71, lines 1–36)	The old woman laughed as she went upstairs To tell her mistress that her husband was home. She ran up the steps, lifting her knees high, And, bending over Penelope, she said: "Wake up, dear child, so you can see for yourself What you have yearned for day in and day out. Odysseus has come home, after all this time, And has killed those men who tried to marry you And who ravaged your house and bullied your son." And Penelope, alert now and wary: "Dear nurse, the gods have driven you crazy. The gods can make even the wise mad, Just as they often make the foolish wise. Now they have wrecked your usually sound mind. Why do you mock me and my sorrowful heart, Waking me from sleep to tell me this nonsense– And such a sweet sleep. It sealed my eyelids. I haven't slept like that since the day Odysseus Left for Ilion–that accursed city. Now go back down to the hall. If any of the others had told me this And wakened me from sleep, I would have Sent her back with something to be sorry about! You can thank your old age for this at least." And Eurycleia, the loyal nurse: "I am not mocking you, child. Odysseus Really is here. He's come home, just as I say. He's the stranger they all insulted in the great hall. Telemachus has known all along, but had The self-control to hide his father's plans Until he could pay the arrogant bastards back." Penelope felt a sudden pang of joy. She leapt From her bed and flung her arms around the old woman, And with tears in her eyes she said to her: "Dear nurse, if it is true, if he really has Come back to his house, tell me how He laid his hands on the shameless suitors, One man alone against all of that mob." (Lombardo 215–16, lines 1–38)

Name

Date Class

<table>
<tr><th colspan="3">Reconciliation</th></tr>
<tr><td colspan="3">Penelope started trembling with joy. She burst into tears and threw her arms around Odysseus. "It's you!" she said. "Oh, Odysseus, it's really you! Don't be angry with me. No one has cut through the bedpost. But I've always been afraid that someone would come here and trick me by pretending to be you. So I thought up this plan to make sure I couldn't be deceived. Because no one knows the secret of the bed except you and me." (Cross 169)</td></tr>
<tr><th>#1: 1891 (prose)</th><th>#2: 1900 (prose)</th><th>#3: 1932 (prose)</th></tr>
<tr><td>As he spoke thus, her knees grew feeble and her very soul, when she recognized the tokens which Odysseus exactly told. Then bursting into tears, she ran straight toward him, threw her arms around Odysseus' neck, and kissed his face, and said: "Odysseus, do not scorn me! Ever before, you were the wisest of mankind. The gods have sent us sorrow, and grudged our staying side by side to share the joys of youth and reach the threshold of old age. But do not be angry with me now or take it ill that when I first saw you I did not greet you thus; for the heart within my breast was always trembling. I feared some man may come and cheat me with his tale. Many a man makes wicked schemes for gain." (Palmer 364)</td><td>When she heard the sure proofs Ulysses now gave her, she fairly broke down. She flew weeping to his side, flung her arms about his neck, and kissed him. "Do not be angry with me Ulysses," she cried, "you, who are the wisest of mankind. We have suffered, both of us. Heaven has denied us the happiness of spending our youth, and of growing old, together; do not then be aggrieved or take it amiss that I did not embrace you thus as soon as I saw you. I have been shuddering all the time through fear that someone might come here and deceive me with a lying story; for there are many very wicked people going about. (Butler)</td><td>As Odysseus had run on, furnishing her with proof too solid for rejection, her knees trembled, and her heart. She burst into tears, she ran to him, she flung her arms about his neck and kissed his head and cried, "My Odysseus, forgive me this time too, you who were of old more comprehending than any man of men. The Gods gave us sorrow for our portion, and in envy denied us the happiness of being together throughout our days, from the heat of youth to the shadow of old age. Be not angry with me, therefore, nor resentful, because at first sight I failed to fondle you thus. The heart within me ever shook for terror of being cheated by some man's lie, so innumerable are those who plot to serve greedy ends. (Lawrence)</td></tr>
<tr><th>#4: 1961 (verse)</th><th colspan="2">#5: 2007 (verse)</th></tr>
<tr><td>Their secret! as she heard it told, her kneesgrew
tremulous and weak, her heart failed her.
With eyes brimming tears she ran to him,
throwing her arms around his neck, and kissed him,
murmuring:
"Do not rage at me, Odysseus!
No one ever matched your caution! Think
what difficulty the gods gave: they denied us
life together in our prime and f lowering years,
kept us from crossing into age together.
Forgive me, don't be angry. I could not
welcome you with love on sight! I armed myself
long ago against the frauds of men,
impostors who might come–and all those many
whose underhanded ways bring evil on!
(Fitzgerald 576, lines 208–20)</td><td colspan="2">In tears, she ran straight to him, threw her arms
Around him, kissed his face, and said:
"Don't be angry with me, Odysseus. You,
Of all men, know how the world goes.
It is the gods who gave us sorrow, the gods
Who begrudged us a life together, enjoying
Our youth and arriving side by side
To the threshold of old age. Don't hold it against me
That when I first saw you I didn't welcome you
As I do now. My heart has been cold with fear
That an imposter would come and deceive me.
There are many who scheme for ill-gotten gains.
(Lombardo 221–22, lines 214–25)</td></tr>
</table>

Name

Date Class

Handout 21C: Character and Context Peer Review

Directions: Review and provide feedback to your partner about his/her hero, setting, and conflict.

Describe your partner's **hero** (appearance, personality, skills, strengths, gifts, weaknesses, obstacles). What other information should the author provide about this hero?
Describe your partner's **setting** (location, time period, weather, seasons, challenges, dangers, advantages). What other information do you wish were provided about this setting?
Describe the **conflict** in your partner's myth. Who is involved and what is the issue? What other information do you wish were provided about the conflict?

Name

Date Class

Handout 23A: Listening and Reading–*Ramayana*

Directions: Follow the directions for each step below.

1. Create a larger version of the following table on a sheet of paper or in your Response Journal as directed by your teacher.

	Listening	Reading
What do I "hear"?		
What do I "see"?		
What do I wonder?		

2. Listen to the recording of an excerpt of Griffith's translation from "Book VI" (Sita's Response"), and complete the "Listening" column in the table.

3. Read the text of the same excerpt of Griffith's translation from "Book VI" (page 1 of Handout 23B), and complete the "Reading" column in the table.

4. Review your completed table and then write at least two explanatory paragraphs (again on a sheet of paper or in your Response Journal as directed by your teacher) in which you compare and contrast your experiences of listening to the text and reading the text. What was the same about those experiences with this excerpt of *Ramayana*? What was different?

Name

Date Class

Handout 23B: Translations of Valmiki's *Ramayana*

Directions: Please follow the directions on Handout 23A for the first translation of "Sita's Response." Then turn to the next page for directions about the homework with the remaining translations contained in this handout

संप्राप्तमवमानं यस्तेजसा न प्रमार्जति ।
कस्तस्य पौरुषेणार्थो महताप्यल्पचेतसः ॥ ६-११५-६

Sita's Response
The blue prince rejected Sita for having spent so many nights in another man's home. The princess felt so disgraced and heartbroken that she asked Lakshman to build her a cremation fire. Sita then spoke so everyone could hear. She declared that if she were innocent, she would be unharmed by the flames. Otherwise, she would gladly let herself perish before anyone who questioned her honor. Sita bravely walked into the fire and stood in its center. (Patel 114)

#1: 1870 (verse)

Struck down with overwhelming shame
She shrank within her trembling frame.
Each word of Ráma's like a dart
Had pierced the lady to the heart;
And from her sweet eyes unrestrained
The torrent of her sorrows, rained.
Her weeping eyes at length she dried,
And thus mid choking sobs replied:
'Canst thou, a high-born prince, dismiss
A high-born dame with speech like this?
Such words befit the meanest hind,
Not princely birth and generous mind,
By all my virtuous life I swear
I am not what thy words declare.
If some are faithless, wilt thou find
No love and truth in womankind?
Doubt others if thou wilt, but own
The truth which all my life has shown.
If, when the giant seized his prey,
Within his hated arms I lay,
And felt the grasp I dreaded, blame
Fate and the robber, not thy dame.
What could a helpless woman do?
My heart was mine and still was true,
Why when Hanúmán sent by thee
Sought Lanká's town across the sea,
Couldst thou not give, O lord of men,
Thy sentence of rejection then?
Then in the presence of the chief
Death, ready death, had brought relief,
Nor had I nursed in woe and pain
This lingering life, alas in vain.
Then hadst thou shunned the fruitless strife
Nor jeopardied thy noble life,
But spared thy friends and bold allies
Their vain and weary enterprise
Is all forgotten, all? my birth,
Named Janak's child, from fostering earth?
That day of triumph when a maid
My trembling hand in thine I laid?
My meek obedience to thy will,
My faithful love through joy and ill,
That never failed at duty's call–
O King, is all forgotten, all?'
To Lakshman then she turned and spoke
While sobs and sighs her utterance broke:
'Sumitrá's son, a pile prepare,
'My refuge in my dark despair.
I will not live to bear this weight
Of shame, forlorn and desolate.
The kindled fire my woes shall end
And be my best and surest friend.'
His mournful eyes the hero raised
And wistfully on Ráma gazed,
In whose stern look no ruth was seen,
No mercy for the weeping queen.
No chieftain dared to meet those eyes,
To pray, to question or advise.
The word was passed, the wood was piled
And fain to die stood Janak's child.
She slowly paced around her lord.
The Gods with reverent act adored,
Then raising suppliant hands the dame
Prayed humbly to the Lord of Flame;
'As this fond heart by virtue swayed
From Raghu's son has never strayed,
So, universal witness, Fire
Protect my body on the pyre,
As Raghu's son has idly laid
This charge on Sítá, hear and aid.'
She ceased: and fearless to the last
Within the flame's wild fury passed.
Then rose a piercing cry from all
Dames, children, men, who saw her fall
Adorned with gems and gay attire
Beneath the fury of the fire. (Griffith 499)

Name

Date Class

Homework Directions: Read and annotate the two additional translations of "Sita's Response" provided on this page. Then read and annotate all of the "Reconciliation" translations on the next page.

Sita's Response	
The blue prince rejected Sita for having spent so many nights in another man's home. The princess felt so disgraced and heartbroken that she asked Lakshman to build her a cremation fire. Sita then spoke so everyone could hear. She declared that if she were innocent, she would be unharmed by the flames. Otherwise, she would gladly let herself perish before anyone who questioned her honor. Sita bravely walked into the fire and stood in its center. (Patel 114)	
#2: 1957 (prose)	**#3: 2009 (prose)**
Sita looked at Rama. Her eyes flashed fire. "Unworthy words have you spoken!" she said. "My ears have heard them and my heart is broken. The uncultured may speak such words but not one nobly born and brought up like you. Your anger, it seems, has destroyed your understanding. My lord does not remember the family from which I come. Janaka, the great seer, was my father and he brought me up. Is it my fault that the wicked Rakshasa seized me by force and imprisoned me? But since this is how you look at it, there is but one course open to me." Then turning to Lakshmana, "Fetch the faggots, Lakshmana, and kindle a fire," she said. Lakshmana, who had been watching Rama's behavior in dismay and indignation turned to look at Rama's face seeking his orders, but Rama did not say 'No' to Sita's request nor show any sign of softening. Obeying Sita, Lakshmana kindled a big fire and the princess, with eyes fixed on the ground, circumambulated her lord and exclaimed: "Ye Gods, I bow before you. Oh rishis, I bow to you. Oh Agni, you at least know my purity and will take me as your own!" With these words she jumped into the flames. (Rajagopalachari 196–97)	Hearing the harsh words with indignation, spoken by Rama, which caused her hair to stand on end, Seetha became very much perturbed. Hearing the terrific words of her husband, which were never actually heard by her before, amidst a large gathering of people, Seetha stood bent low with shame. As though her own limbs were pierced by those words, which were arrow-like with pointed splinters, Seetha shed profuse tears. Then, wiping clean her face, which was bathed in tears, she spoke the following words slowly, in a stammering voice to her husband. "O valiant Rama! Why are you speaking such harsh words, which are violent to hear for me, like a common man speaking to a common woman?".... "O king! Hanuma, the great hero, was sent by you as your search-agent. Why I, who was still in Lanka, was not abandoned then itself?" "O hero! Life would have been given up by me, when deserted by you; immediately on hearing the message (conveying your desertion) before the eyes of the monkey." "This wasteful endeavour (in the form of crossing over to Lanka and waging war against the mighty Ravana, keeping your life in jeopardy), would not have been there, nor would have your friends been put to such fruitless hardship." "O excellent king! You, however, like a feeble man, gave priority to womanliness, conforming yourself to just an emotion of anger." "O knower of virtuous conduct! My birth was from Janaka in disguise; but was actually from the earth. My sacred birth of such a high degree, was not honoured by you." "My hand taken (by you as a bride) in our childhood was not duly recognized by you. My devotion, my chastity and all have been ignored by you." Seetha, thus speaking, weeping and stammering with tears, said to Lakshmana, who was sad and engaged in thoughtfulness (as follows): "O Lakshmana! Create a pile of fire, for me, which is a remedy for this disaster. I no longer wish to survive, smitten as am with false blames." .... Thus speaking, Seetha walking around the fire-god, with her mind free from hesitation, entered the blazing fire.... (Murthy)

Name

Date Class

Reconciliation

Rama kneeled before Sita and apologized for his behavior. As he explained everything that he'd done to find her, Sita's heart softened and she forgave him. The two gazed at each other with an abundance of love as the crowd cheered . . . Times have changed, as have customs, but love has always been complicated. (Patel 117)

#1: 1870 (verse)	#2: 1957 (prose)	#3: 2009 (prose)
...Still stood the king in thoughtful mood And tears of joy his eyes bedewed. Then to the best of Gods the best Of warrior chiefs his mind expressed: 'Twas meet that mid the thousands here The searching fire my queen should clear; For long within the giant's bower She dwelt the vassal of his power. For else had many a slanderous tongue Reproaches on mine honour flung, And scorned the king who, love-impelled, His consort from the proof withheld. No doubt had I, but surely knew That Janak's child was pure and true, That, come what might, in good and ill Her faithful heart was with me still. I knew that Rávan could not wrong My queen whom virtue made so strong. I knew his heart would sink and fail, Nor dare her honour to assail, As Ocean, when he raves and roars. Fears to o'erleap his bounding shores. Now to the worlds her truth is shown, And Sítá is again mine own. Thus proved before unnumbered eyes, On her pure fame no shadow lies. As heroes to their glory cleave, Mine own dear spouse I ne'er will leave.' He ceased: and clasped in fond embrace On his dear breast she hid her face. (Griffith 500)	Rama said to Brahma: "Who am I? All that I know and can tell is that I am Rama, son of Dasaratha. You know who I am and whence I came and more. It is you who must inform me." Saying this to Brahma, Rama accepted Sita fire-proved. "Think you that I did not know your irreproachable purity? This ordeal was to satisfy the people. Without it, they would say that Rama, blinded by love, behaved with a strange weakness and broke the rule of well-brought-up men." So saying he drew her to his side. (Rajagopalachari 197)	Rama, the excellent among the eloquent, whose mind was set on virtue, with a pleasant mind to hear the aforesaid speech, reflected for a while, his eyes, entirely filled with tears of joy. Hearing those words, the courageous Rama of great prowess and the foremost of those upholding the virtue, replied to the fire-god, the best of gods. "Seetha certainly deserves this pure factory ordeal in the eyes of the people in as much as this blessed woman had resided for a long time indeed in the gynaecium of Ravana. "The world would chatter against me, saying that Rama, the son of Dasaratha, was really foolish and that his mind was dominated by lust, if I accept Seetha without examining her with regard to her chastity." "I also know that Seetha, the daughter of Janaka, who ever revolves in my mind, is undivided in her affection to me." "Ravana could not violate this wide-eyed woman, protected as she was by her own splendour, any more than an ocean would transgress its bounds." "In order to convince the three worlds, I, whose refugee is truth, ignored Seetha while she was entering the fire." "The evil-minded Ravana was not able to lay his violent hands, even in thought, on the unobtainable Seetha, who was blazing like a flaming tongue of fire." "This auspicious woman could not give way to the sovereignty, existing in the gynaecium of Ravana, in as much as Seetha is not different from me, even as sunlight is not different from the sun." "Seetha, the daughter of Janaka, is completely pure in her character, in all the three worlds and can no longer be renounced by me, as a good name cannot be cast aside by a prudent man." The salutary advice of you all, the affectionate guardians of the world, who are saying what is conducive to our good, must be certainly carried out by me." Saying thus and getting reunited with her beloved Seetha, the victorious and highly illustrious Rama, a scion of Raghu dynasty, who was endowed with a great strength and deserved happiness and was being glorified by his exploits, performed by his own self, experienced joy. (Murthy)

Name

Date Class

Handout 23C: Presentation Planner

Directions: Use the table below to draft the slide presentation about your hero and the context of your original monomyth.
Remember!

- Order information logically.
- Integrate visuals to make information more engaging.
- Limit the amount of text that viewers have to read.
- Spell words correctly.

Slide Number	Character, Setting, or Conflict?	Notes about Ideas and Images
1		
2		
3		
4		
5		
6		

Name

Date Class

Handout 23D: Optional Fluency Practice 4

Directions:

1. Day 1: Read the text carefully and annotate to help you read fluently.
2. Each day:
   a. Practice reading the text three to five times.
   b. Evaluate your progress by placing a √+, √, or √- in each unshaded box.
   c. Ask someone (adult or peer) to listen and evaluate you as well.
3. Last day: Respond to the self-reflection questions.

She slowly paced around her lord.
The Gods with reverent act adored,
Then raising suppliant hands the dame
Prayed humbly to the Lord of Flame;
'As this fond heart by virtue swayed
From Raghu's son has never strayed,
So, universal witness, Fire
Protect my body on the pyre,
As Raghu's son has idly laid
This charge on Sítá, hear and aid.'
She ceased: and fearless to the last
Within the flame's wild fury passed.
Then rose a piercing cry from all
Dames, children, men, who saw her fall
Adorned with gems and gay attire Beneath the fury of the fire. (Griffith 499)

Name

Date Class

Student Performance Checklist:	Day 1		Day 2		Day 3		Day 4	
	You	Listener*	You	Listener*	You	Listener*	You	Listener*
Accurately read the passage 3–5 times.								
Read with appropriate phrasing and pausing.								
Read with appropriate expression.								
Read articulately at a good pace and an audible volume.								

*Adult or peer

Self-reflection: What choices did you make when deciding how to read this passage, and why? What would you like to improve on or try differently next time? (*Thoughtfully answer these questions below.*)

Name

Date Class

Handout 25A: Excerpt from *The Odyssey*

Directions: Use this excerpt from Robert Fagles's translation of "Book 23" ("Reconciliation") of *The Odyssey* for New-Read Assessment 1 (Assessment 25A) as directed.

1 Penelope felt her knees go slack, her heart surrender,
2 recognizing the strong clear signs Odysseus offered.
3 She dissolved in tears, rushed to Odysseus, flung her arms
4 around his neck and kissed his head and cried out,
5 "Odysseus–don't flare up at me now, not you,
6 always the most understanding man alive!
7 The gods, it was the gods who sent us sorrow–
8 they grudged[1] us both a life in each other's arms
9 from the heady zest of youth to the stoop of old age.
10 But don't fault me, angry with me now because I failed,
11 at the first glimpse, to greet you, hold you, so ...
12 In my heart of hearts I always cringed with fear
13 some fraud might come, beguile[2] me with his talk;
14 the world is full of the sort,
15 cunning ones who plot their own dark ends."

(Fagles 387)

[1]*to not want to give or allow*
[2]*to deceive or cheat by using lies or tricks*

Name

Date Class

Handout 25B: Presentation Peer Edit

Directions: Review and provide feedback to your partner about his/her technology-based presentation draft.

1. What is the order of the information in this presentation? Is this order logical? What suggestions can you offer to improve this?
2. What visuals are included in this presentation? What other images could help make the presentation more interesting? What suggestions can you offer to improve this?
3. How much text do viewers have to read? Does this feel like a reasonable amount? What suggestions can you offer to improve this?
4. Are all words spelled correctly? Record any that are misspelled.

Name

Date Class

Handout 25C: Restrictive Elements

Directions: Underline the restrictive element in each sentence, and then respond to the final question.

1. The twelve men who were the bravest and best were ordered to accompany Odysseus.

2. The man who could lift the bow of Shiva would win Sita's hand in marriage.

3. The boast that Odysseus yelled to Polyphemus ended up costing him greatly.

4. Aeolus tied all the winds that would have blown Odysseus off course into a bag.

5. What does a restrictive element do in a sentence?

Name

Date Class

Handout 28A: "A Practical Guide to Joseph Campbell's *The Hero with a Thousand Faces*"[1]

Directions: Use this memo written by Christopher Vogler for New-Read Assessment 2 (Assessment 28A) as directed.

"There are only two or three human stories, and they go on repeating themselves as fiercely as if they had never happened before." ~Willa Cather

INTRODUCTION

1 In the long run, one of the most influential books of the 20th century may turn out to be Joseph
2 Campbell's THE HERO WITH A THOUSAND FACES.

3 The book and the ideas in it are having a major impact on writing and story-telling, but above all
4 on movie-making. Filmmakers like John Boorman, George Miller, Steven Spielberg, George
5 Lucas, and Francis Coppola owe their successes in part to the ageless patterns that Joseph
6 Campbell identifies in the book.

7 The ideas Campbell presents in this and other books are an excellent set of analytical[2] tools.

8 With them you can almost always determine what's wrong with a story that's floundering[3]; and
9 you can find a better solution to almost any story problem by examining the pattern laid out in
10 the book.

11 There's nothing new in the book. The ideas in it are older than the Pyramids, older than
12 Stonehenge, older than the earliest cave painting.

13 Campbell's contribution was to gather the ideas together, recognize them, articulate[4] them, and
14 name them. He exposes the pattern for the first time, the pattern that lies behind every story

[1]*From Vogler, Christopher. "A Practical Guide to Joseph Campbell's The Hero with a Thousand Faces." Storytech Literary Consulting. Storytech, 1985. Web. 1 July 2016. Vogler, Christopher. The Writer's Journey: Mythic Structure for Writers. 3rd Edition. Studio City, CA: Michael Wiese Productions, 2007.*
[2]***analytical:** resulting from a careful study of the parts of something in order to understand more about the whole*
[3]***floundering**: moving forward in a confused or clumsy way*
[4]***articulate**: to speak or express oneself in a clear way*

Name

Date Class

15 ever told.

16 Campbell, now 82, is a vigorous lover of mythology and the author of many books on the
17 subject. For many years he has taught, written, and lectured about the myths of all cultures in all
18 times. THE HERO WITH A THOUSAND FACES is the clearest statement of his observations on
19 the most persistent theme in all of oral traditions and recorded literature–the myth of the hero.

20 In his study of world hero myths Campbell discovered that they are all basically the same story–
21 retold endlessly in infinite variations. He found that all story-telling, consciously or not, follows
22 the ancient patterns of myth, and that all stories, from the crudest jokes to the highest flights of
23 literature, can be understood in terms of the hero myth; the "monomyth" whose principles he
24 lays out in the book.

25 The theme of the hero myth is universal[5], occurring in every culture, in every time; it is as
26 infinitely varied as the human race itself; and yet its basic form remains the same, an incredibly
27 tenacious[6] set of elements that spring in endless repetition from the deepest reaches of the mind
28 of man.

29 Campbell's thinking runs parallel to that of Swiss psychologist Carl Jung, who wrote of the
30 "archetypes" – constantly repeating characters who occur in the dreams of all people and the
31 myths of all cultures.

32 Jung suggested that these archetypes are a reflection of aspects[7] of the human mind–that our
33 personalities divide themselves into these characters to play out the drama of our lives.

34 He noticed a strong correspondence[8] between his patients' dream or fantasy figures and the
35 common archetypes of mythology, and he suggested that both were coming from a deeper

[5]**universal**: *for or affecting everyone*
[6]**tenacious**: *holding on or tending to hold on strongly or persistently*
[7]**aspects**: *elements or parts*
[8]**correspondence**: *agreement or similarity between or among things*

Name

Date Class

36 source, in the "collective unconscious" of the human race.

37 The repeating characters of the hero myth such as the young hero, the wise old man or woman,
38 the shape-shifting woman or man, and the shadowy antagonist are identical with the archetypes
39 of the human mind, as revealed in dreams. That's why myths, and stories constructed on the
40 mythological model, strike us as psychologically[9] true.

41 Such stories are true models of the workings of the human mind, true maps of the psyche[10].
42 They are psychologically valid and realistic even when they portray fantastic, impossible, unreal
43 events.

44 This accounts for the universal power of such stories. Stories built on the model of the hero myth
45 have an appeal that can be felt by everyone, because they spring from a universal source in the
46 collective unconscious, and because they reflect universal concerns. They deal with the child-like
47 but universal questions: Who am I? Where did I come from? Where will I go when I die? What is
48 good and what is evil? What must I do about it? What will tomorrow be like? Where did
49 yesterday go? Is there anybody else out there?

50 The idea imbedded in mythology and identified by Campbell in THE HERO WITH A
51 THOUSAND FACES can be applied to understanding any human problem. They are a great key
52 to life as well as being a major tool for dealing more effectively with a mass audience.

53 If you want to understand the ideas behind the hero myth, there's no substitute for actually
54 reading Campbell's book. It's an experience that has a way of changing people. It's also a good
55 idea to read a lot of myths, but it amounts to the same thing since Campbell is a master story-
56 teller who delights in illustrating his points with examples from the rich storehouse of
57 mythology.

[9]**psychologically**: *having to do with the mind or emotions*
[10]**psyche**: *the human soul or spirit*

Name

Date Class

58 Campbell gives a condensed version of the basic hero myth in chapter IV, "The Keys,", of THE
59 HERO WITH A THOUSAND FACES. I've taken the liberty of amending[11] the outline slightly,
60 trying to reflect some of the common themes in movies, illustrated with examples from
61 contemporary films. I'm re-telling the hero myth in my own way, and you should feel free to do
62 the same. Every story-teller bends the myth to his or her own purpose. That's why the hero has a
63 thousand faces...

• •

64 The hero's journey, once more: The hero is introduced in his ORDINARY WORLD where he
65 receives the CALL TO ADVENTURE. He is RELUCTANT at first to CROSS THE FIRST
66 THRESHOLD where he eventually encounters TESTS, ALLIES and ENEMIES. He reaches the
67 INNERMOST CAVE where he endures the SUPREME ORDEAL. He SEIZES THE SWORD or
68 the treasure and is pursued on the ROAD BACK to his world. He is RESURRECTED and
69 transformed by his experience. He RETURNS to his ordinary world with a treasure, boon, or
70 ELIXIR to benefit his world.

• •

71 As with any formula, there are pitfalls[12] to be avoided. Following the guidelines of myth too
72 rigidly can lead to a stiff, unnatural structure, and there is the danger of being too obvious. The
73 hero myth is a skeleton that should be masked with the details of the individual story, and the
74 structure should not call attention to itself. The order of the hero's stages as given here is only
75 one of many variations–the stages can be deleted, added to, and drastically re-shuffled without
76 losing any of their power.

77 The values of the myth are what's important. The images of the basic version–young heroes
78 seeking magic swords from old wizards, fighting evil dragons in deep caves, etc.–are just
79 symbols and can be changed infinitely to suit the story at hand.

[11]**amending**: *to change or add*
[12]**pitfalls**: *unexpected or hidden dangers*

Name

Date Class

80 The myth is easily translated to contemporary dramas, comedies, romances, or action-
81 adventures by substituting modern equivalents for the symbolic figures and props of the hero
82 story. The Wise Old Man may be a real shaman or wizard, but he can also be any kind of mentor
83 or teacher, doctor or therapist, crusty but benign[13] boss, tough but fair top sergeant, parent,
84 grandfather, etc. Modern heroes may not be going into caves and labyrinths to fight their
85 mythical beasts, but they do enter an innermost cave by going into space, to the bottom of the
86 sea, into their own minds, or into the depths of a modern city.

87 The myth can be used to tell the simplest comic book story or the most sophisticated drama. It
88 grows and matures as new experiments are tried within its basic framework. Changing the sex
89 and ages of the basic characters only makes it more interesting and allows for ever more
90 complex webs of understanding to be spun among them. The essential characters can be
91 combined or divided into several figures to show different aspects of the same idea. The myth is
92 infinitely flexible, capable of endless variation without sacrificing any of its magic, and it will
93 outlive us all.

[13]**benign**: *possessing or displaying kindness or gentleness*

Name ____________________

Date __________ Class __________

Handout 28B: Archetype Development

Directions: Use the questions below to help you create some of the archetypal characters for your monomyth.

Archetype and Name	How would you describe this character? (Optional: sketch your character)	How does the hero meet this character?	How does this character help the hero overcome his/her flaw?
ALLY __________			
MENTOR __________			
SHADOW __________			**How does the shadow try to use the hero's flaw to defeat him/her?**

Name

Date Class

Handout 29A: Joseph Campbell's Hero[1]

Directions: Read the excerpt from Bill Moyer's interview with Joseph Campbell below and respond to the questions with your partner.

BILL MOYERS: *Why are there so many stories of the hero or of heroes in mythology?*

JOSEPH CAMPBELL: *Well, because that's what's worth writing about. I mean, even in popular novel writing, you see, the main character is the hero or heroine, that is to say, someone who has found or achieved or done something beyond the normal range of achievement and experience. A hero properly is someone who has given his life to something bigger than himself or other than himself.*

1. Summarize what Joseph Campbell believes makes someone a hero.

2. Explain how three characters from books, movies, or TV qualify as heroes based on Campbell's definition.

Character Name	What They've Given Their Life to Do

3. What does *normal* mean in this context?

[1]Moyers, Bill. "*Ep. 1: Joseph Campbell and the Power of Myth - The Hero's Adventure.*" Moyers and Company. 8 *Mar.* 2013/1988. *Web.* 11 *June* 2016. http://billmoyers.com/content/ep-1-joseph-campbell-and-the-power-of-myth-the-hero's-adventure-audio/

Name

Date Class

Handout 30A: Presentation Tracker

Directions: Complete the table with information from each group's presentation.

Group Number	Title of Text	How Does This Text Exemplify the Monomyth Genre?
1		
2		
3		

Name

Date Class

Group Number	Title of Text	How Does This Text Exemplify the Monomyth Genre?
4		
5		
6		

Name

Date Class

Handout 31A: End-of-Module Task Resources

Directions: Follow the steps described in the table below and use the noted resources as directed to complete the End-of-Module Task.

Grade 6 Module 2 EOM Task Process			
Step	**Step Description**	**Resources** (*items in bold are included in this handout*)	**✓ When Complete**
1	**GET CLEAR** ▪ Understand the task. ▪ Deconstruct the task exemplars.	▪ Assessment 31A ▪ **Exemplar** ▪ **Peer Review**	
2	**GET STARTED** ▪ Review Rama's and Odysseus's journeys through the twelve stages. ▪ Add or revise your hero, context, and archetypes as needed. ▪ Confer with your peers and teacher as needed.	▪ Handout 9A ▪ Handout 19C ▪ Handout 20A: Context Development ▪ Handout 28A ▪ Response Journal ▪ Responses to FQTs 1, 2, and 4	
3	**PLAN** ▪ Plan at least five of the required stages of your hero's journey, explaining how the hero's flaw impacts them in this stage. ▪ Choose two of those stages to develop into narrative scenes.	▪ Response Journals ▪ Handout 8A ▪ Handout 9B	
4	**DRAFT** ▪ Develop and draft your narrative scenes. ▪ Confer with your peers and teacher as needed.	▪ Handout 6A ▪ Handout 14A ▪ Handout 4C ▪ Vocabulary Journals	
5	**REVIEW** ▪ Complete peer review.	▪ **Peer Review**	
6	**REVISE** ▪ Review and discuss feedback, consulting with your peers and teacher as needed. ▪ Revise the structure, development, style, and conventions of your narrative scenes.	▪ All of the above	

Name

Date Class

7	**PREPARE PRESENTATION** ▪ Annotate for accuracy, phrasing, expression, articulation, pacing, volume, and anything else that will help you read your chosen scene masterfully. ▪ Use technology to create a visual component to enhance and support your presentation.	▪ Guidelines for Technology-Based Presentations in Response Journal	
8	**PRACTICE PRESENTATION** ▪ Rehearse with a partner and use their feedback to improve your performance.	▪ Handout 25B	
9	**SELF ASSESS** ▪ Review Rubric. ▪ Complete Self Checklist.	▪ **Narrative Writing Checklist** ▪ Narrative Writing Rubric	
10	**PRESENT AND SUBMIT** ▪ Make final revisions. ▪ Listen to and evaluate peers' presentations. ▪ Present and submit your monomyth.	▪ **Monomyth Presentations**	

Name

Date Class

Step 1: Deconstruct Exemplar

Character Archetypes in Your Monomyth	
Archetype	**Character Details**
Hero	Brenda Collins is a seventh-grade girl who lives in Prairie, Texas and attends Prairie Middle School. She lives with her dad, who is always busy and stressed out about his job. Brenda is talented at drawing and breakdancing but really struggles with math. She's a good friend to others, even though she's hard on herself. Besides tutoring, she isn't currently allowed to participate in afterschool activities because she has to get home and babysit her little brother Benji. Brenda really wants to get better at math because she doesn't want to have to go to summer school. She'd like to be smarter and have less trouble learning but she doesn't have the confidence to realize that she's smart in different ways. Brenda's flaw is that she has low self-confidence and doesn't think of herself as able to accomplish things. She's really focused on how poorly she's doing in school and doesn't recognize that she's brave and creative. Although Brenda doesn't realize she's a hero, Ms. Thomas, Butterfinger, Dog, and Mama Luna all know that she's capable of doing great things. Brenda will rescue the Tomb of Secrets, keeping the world safe from the Badger King and his army of evil moles. Over the course of her journey, she'll realize that she is brave and creative and has lots of great qualities. Meeting Mama Luna and finding out that Butterfinger, Dog, and Tulip all believe in her helps Brenda believe in herself. She returns home more confident. Brenda even asks her dad to let her take dance lessons again one night a week, now knowing that she is capable of overcoming her challenges in math and that she deserves something fun instead of constantly punishing herself.
Shadow	The Badger King rules Frenesco and frightens everyone into obeying him. He shreds the school library looking for the Tomb of Secrets and is confident he can defend it, even with his limited eyesight. He doesn't expect a human and her dog to come looking for the Tomb and is unprepared for Brenda and Dog. The Badger King tries to intimidate Brenda when she comes for the Tomb of Secrets, insulting her by calling her "measly" and "powerless." Before her journey, Brenda would have backed down or run away when a giant, scary badger called her those things but with Butterfinger, Dog, and Mama Luna on her side, Brenda defeats him.
Mentor	Brenda has had Butterfinger, her cat, since she was a baby. When Brenda refuses to go on the quest to rescue the Tomb of Secrets, Butterfinger reveals that he can speak and explains that he has been helping keep the Tomb safe for many years. He explains that he's too old to go after it now but that he's seen Brenda grow up and he's been training her this whole time to become a hero. Butterfinger knows that Brenda struggles with confidence but he insists that she is the only one capable of carrying out this quest. He convinces her to go with Dog and gives them a map of Frenesco to use on their journey. Mama Luna is a giant, talking raccoon who helps Brenda when she cuts her arm. Mama Luna confirms that Brenda is the right person for this quest, even though Brenda doesn't believe it until meeting Mama Luna. It is in her time spent with Mama Luna that Brenda is able to realize how strong and brave she really is. Mama Luna also gives Brenda a magic flashlight without any instructions about how or when to use it. She promises that Brenda will know when it's time. When Brenda is about to face the Badger King, she hears Mama Luna's voice encouraging her, boosting her up. Brenda uses the flashlight to defeat the Badger King.
Ally	Brenda has a shaggy, old dog named Dog who she's had since her mom mysteriously disappeared. He's usually sleepy and lazy but in this myth, Brenda will learn that Dog can talk and is a lot more adventuresome than she realizes. Dog knows all about the missing Tomb of Secrets and is Brenda's sidekick when she goes to rescue it. Dog believes in Brenda and helps her see how brave and creative she really is. When Brenda's inner monologue starts and she's telling herself how incapable she is, Dog is there to boost her confidence. Tulip is a tiny, talking mouse who wants to escape Frenesco but is too small to do so on her own. She helps Dog and Brenda escape with the Tomb of Secrets and in exchange, Brenda takes her home with them. Tulip understands Brenda's struggle with confidence and shares that she, too, has had to work to recognize her own strength and potential. Tulip and Dog become the best of friends.

Name

Date Class

Stages of a Hero's Journey in Your Monomyth	
Vogler's Stage	**What occurs during this stage in this text?**
Stage 2. Call to Adventure	Brenda sees a strange creature running out of the school and thinks about chasing it, but doesn't think she's fast enough. She hears crying coming from the library. She peeks her head in, sees the library torn apart, and the librarian crying. The librarian, Miss Thomas, explains tearfully that the Tomb of Secrets has been stolen, she was the keeper, and it was supposed to be safe in the school. The Tomb is in unsafe hands, somewhere in Frenesco. Brenda has no idea what Miss Thomas is talking about and because of her low self-confidence, Brenda doesn't think she can help recover the Tomb.
Stage 4. Meeting with the Mentor	Dog calls in Butterfinger, Brenda's very old cat. It turns out both of Brenda's pets can talk and Butterfinger explains why Brenda has to go with dog and rescue the Tomb of Secrets. Butterfinger tells Brenda that he's been working with Miss Thomas for years to keep the Tomb safe but is now too old to go after it himself. He believes in Brenda and Dog and shares with them a map of Frenesco and his wisdom about traveling there. He convinces Brenda that she's his only hope.
Stage 6. Tests, Allies, and Enemies	1. They climb over a mountain of empty water bottles and recyclables. Brenda's foot gets stuck, she tells herself she'll never make it out, but Dog reminds her of the time she got caught in a hammock and how she creatively unwound herself to escape. Dog's story reminds Brenda of how creative she can be and she creates a lever to wedge herself out of the bottles. 2. They have to hang onto a rope swing over a polluted river and Brenda has to face failures from gym class. She falls in, grabs Dog just in time, and scrambles out on opposite side. Brenda realizes that she's stronger than she used to be in gym class. 3. They must sneak past a clan of rats, led by President Fuge, the most powerful rat in Frenesco. While doing so, Brenda overhears President Fuge talk about wrath of the Badger King. Brenda trips and cuts open her arm. She passes out. Brenda regains consciousness in the arms of Mama Luna, a giant, talking raccoon. Mama Luna confirms the importance of Brenda's mission and that she is just the person to rescue the Tomb of Secrets. She gives Brenda a magic flashlight.
Stage 8. The Ordeal	They walk further into tunnel only to realize they're in a badger's lair. This explains the condition of the library. Amongst other treasures lies the Tomb of Secrets. Brenda snatches book, looks around, and is confronted by a furious badger. She screams, runs, and watches Dog attack the badger. Brenda runs at the badger to get Dog to safety, she's flung onto rocks, and hears the flashlight clink on. Brenda uses it to shine in badger's eyes–he starts swinging and catapults her clear out of the lair.
Stage 11. The Resurrection	Brenda, Dog, and Tulip make it to street level. For a moment, Brenda is tempted to run back underground to avoid all the trouble she's about to be in. Then, she remembers all that she's been through and realizes that she can face whatever comes next. They all head back to the middle school to return the Tomb of Secrets. Ms. Thomas is grateful, she calls Brenda's dad and lets her clean up quickly. Brenda's dad is thrilled to see Brenda and Dog and is very relieved. Brenda apologizes to the police and the FBI, Miss Thomas makes up a story that explains everything to them.

Name

Date Class

A Missing Tomb of Secrets

Departure Phase: Call to Adventure Stage

Brenda sighed as she walked down the empty hallway. The other seventh graders, who seemed to have no problem with pre-algebra, never stayed for afterschool tutoring. It's just me that doesn't get it, Brenda thought. I'll never be any good at this. It's amazing I even passed sixth grade.

Just as she turned the corner, Brenda heard loud, thundering footsteps trampling toward the doors. She looked up just in time to see an enormous shadowy shape sprint out the front doors. For a moment, Brenda considered chasing the dark figure but how would she ever catch it? I'm not a fast runner and I'm certainly not athletic. How could I possibly keep up with that thing? I can't believe I even thought about doing that.

Then she heard a muffled crying noise. She stopped, frozen in her tracks, trying to determine where the whimpering was coming from. It was coming from the library. She peered in, her eyes searching in the murky darkness for the source of the sounds.

When her eyes adjusted to the shadowy room, Brenda was startled to see that almost every book in the room had been thrown from the shelves and scattered across the floor. Pages littered the carpet; books were shredded as though giant claws had gone on a rampage through the shelves. Brenda stepped entirely into the darkness, toward the continuing, hiccupping sobs. "Miss Thomas?" she called hesitantly.

"Brenda Collins?" came a muffled sniffle from behind the front desk. Peering behind the desk, Brenda saw the school's tiny librarian collapsed between the desk and the wall. Brenda reached out to her and Miss Thomas clamped a surprisingly strong hand on each of Brenda's wrists.

"Brenda, you must go after them! They have the Tomb of Secrets!" Miss Thomas yanked her closer and whispered urgently, "It must be protected, Brenda. There's no time to lose. He's taking it to Frenesco!" Confused, Brenda shook her head. Miss Thomas insistently declared, "It's up to you now. Go recover the Tomb before it's too late!"

"Miss Thomas, I'm not a hero. I can't help with this, I'm barely passing seventh grade. How could I ever be the one to do this?" Brenda gasped as the tiny woman released her grip and collapsed back onto the floor. Brenda stumbled back in shock as Miss Thomas' eyes closed, she felt her heart start to thunder in her chest as she dug in her bag for her phone and dialed 911.

Name

Date Class

The Badger King

Initiation Phase: The Ordeal Stage

Dog and Brenda's footsteps echoed off the damp, cement tunnels. Brenda scuffed her foot in a dark puddle and felt cold water ooze into her shoe. She shivered. Dog stopped suddenly and pointed with his nose toward their left. Brenda leaned in to look, seeing a high ceilinged cavern filled with towering piles of old books, mounds of papers and trash, and a dark, hunched over form with his back to them. As Brenda looked closer, she saw a shimmering, light blue book on top of one of the mountainous piles. It was the Tomb of Secrets!

This was her moment. Brenda felt the same tickle of insecurity start to twist around in her stomach. I can't do this, she thought. I'll never make it out of here with that book. I've endangered Dog. I've terrified my dad. All of this because I thought for a second I was brave. Overwhelmed by her worries, Brenda stopped. She closed her fingers around the cool metal of the flashlight Mama Luna had given her. She heard Mama Luna's velvety voice in her mind, "You are brave and strong, Brenda. You're the one we can count on to make everything right." Brenda opened her eyes and saw Dog, who smiled reassuringly and nudged her forward with his shaggy brown head, looking as if he knew what she was thinking.

After taking a deep breath, Brenda nodded to Dog and they crept closer. The dark form, who was mindlessly humming to itself, was hunched over a large, yellowed, old book. Brenda prayed that her footsteps stayed silent as she tiptoed around puddles, getting closer by the moment to the shiny blue book. She pulled herself up onto the trash pile underneath the Tomb and finally, with shaking fingers, slid it into her hands and then her backpack. As she zipped it shut, the zipper let out a long wheeze and the dark form whipped around in her direction.

"You shall not take my Tomb of Secrets, you measly little human! I will squash your cowardly skull between my teeth! How could a tiny, powerless creature like you defeat the mighty Badger King?" howled the hostile creature. He stood up on his hind legs, exposing a black, furry belly and reached for her with long talons. His red beady eyes glowed with fury and the white stripe on his nose seemed to quiver as he roared and gnashed his teeth. This was the notorious Badger King!

"No!" shouted Brenda, surprised at the confidence of her own voice. "Stay back. We're taking the Tomb of Secrets back where it belongs." The Badger King replied with a gritty snarl and lunged at them. Brenda stood her ground and calmly clicked on Mama Luna's flashlight. The bright light stunned the badger; at the same time, the walls of the cavern began to quiver and then shake. Books tumbled from their piles, stones fell from the ceiling, and Brenda shouted to Dog, "RUN!"

Seconds later, the walls of the cavern collapsed, rattling the tunnel floor like an earthquake. Brenda and Dog kept sprinting until they could hear the river again. They sank to the ground, exhausted. Dog looked over at Brenda proudly, "You did it, Brenda. I knew you could." Brenda breathed a sigh of relief as she rested her head on Dog's furry shoulder. Then, she patted the heavy book in her backpack. She really had done it. The Tomb of Secrets was safe.

Name

Date Class

Steps 1 and 5: Peer Review

Directions: Read your partner's narrative, and respond to the questions below to provide feedback help your partner improve his/her writing.

Content Review	
Writer of Narrative	Reviewer of Narrative
1. How effectively is **context** established in this scene? What suggestions do you have to make this more effective?	
2. How effective is the **sequencing of events** in this scene; do the events unfold naturally and logically? What suggestions do you have to make this more effective?	
4. How effectively are **transition words**, **phrases**, and **clauses** used to help convey sequence and to signal shifts in chronology and setting? What suggestions do you have to make this more effective?	

Name

Date Class

5. How effective is the writer's use of the following **narrative techniques**? What suggestions do you have to make this more effective?
Dialogue, Inner Monologue, Narration
Descriptive Details and Sensory Language
Pacing

6. How effectively is the scene brought to **conclusion**? What suggestions do you have to make this more effective?

Name

Date Class

7. Overall, how effectively does this scene exemplify its stage of the hero's journey? What suggestions do you have to make this more effective?

8. How effectively is the hero's flaw incorporated into this scene? What suggestions do you have to make this more effective?

9. What other comments, questions, or suggestions do you have to improve this draft?

Name

Date Class

Style and Conventions Editing Form		
	Yes	No
1. Are all pronouns in the correct case (subjective, objective, or possessive)?		
How could this be improved?		
2. Does the scene contain nonrestrictive elements that add information to the sentences?		
How could this be improved?		
3. Are the nonrestrictive elements correctly punctuated with commas, parentheses, or dashes?		
What punctuation was used to set off nonrestrictive elements? How could this be improved?		
4. Does the scene contain an intensive pronoun?		
What effect does the intensive pronoun have on the sentence? How could this be improved?		
5. How effectively does the narrative follow the conventions of standard written English? Note where you see convention, spelling, punctuation, or grammar errors.		

Name

Date Class

Step 10: Narrative Writing Checklist

Directions: Use this checklist to revise your writing. Mark + for "yes" and Δ for "needs improvement." Ask someone (adult or peer) to evaluate your writing as well.

	Self +/ Δ	Peer +/ Δ	Teacher +/ Δ
Structure			
▪ I respond to all parts of the prompt.			
▪ I establish a context for my narrative.			
▪ I organize my events according to a narrative arc.			
▪ I use transition words, phrases, or clauses to show changes in time or setting.			
▪ My conclusion follows from the events, providing resolution.			
Development			
▪ I include narrative techniques (dialogue, pacing, description).			
▪ I incorporate descriptive details and sensory language.			
Style			
▪ I use a variety of sentence patterns (simple, compound, complex, compound-complex) to add clarity and interest.			
▪ I use precise words and phrases to describe what happened.			
▪ I use vocabulary words that are specific and vivid.			
▪ I write precisely and concisely, without using unnecessary words.			
▪ My writing style is appropriate for the audience.			
Conventions			
▪ I use correct pronoun case.			
▪ I include intensive pronouns to add emphasis to nouns.			
▪ I include nonrestrictive elements using commas, parentheses, and/or dashes to add detail to sentences and enhance interest.			
▪ I use correct spelling			
Total # of checks			

Name

Date Class

Step 11: Monomyth Presentations

Directions: Complete the table for each myth presentation as you listen.

Student Name	Hero, Other Characters, and Archetypes	Stages of a Hero's Journey and Themes

Name

Date Class

Which of your peers' myths do you think was the most effective example of the monomyth genre and why?

Name

Date Class

Handout 32A: Adding Dashes

Directions: Read the excerpt from the End-of-Module Task exemplar narrative. Use a caret (^) to add one or more dashes to the story. You may also choose to include additional words.

Just as she turned the corner, Brenda heard loud, thundering footsteps trampling toward the doors. She looked up just in time to see an enormous shadowy shape sprint out the front doors. For a moment, Brenda considered chasing the dark figure but how would she ever catch it? *I'm not a fast runner and I'm certainly not athletic. How could I possibly keep up with that thing? I can't believe I even thought about doing that.*

Name

Date Class

Handout 33A: Adding Nonrestrictive Elements

Directions:

1. Read the excerpt from the End-of-Module Task exemplar narrative below and underline all of the nouns.

Dog and Brenda's footsteps echoed off the damp, cement tunnels. Brenda scuffed her foot in a dark puddle and felt cold water ooze into her shoe. She shivered. Dog stopped suddenly and pointed with his nose toward their left. Brenda leaned in to look, seeing a high ceilinged cavern filled with towering piles of old books, mounds of papers and trash, and a dark, hunched over form with his back to them. As Brenda looked closer, she saw a shimmering, light blue book on top of one of the mountainous piles. It was the Tomb of Secrets!

2. Add six of the different underlined nouns to the first column of the table below and complete the remaining columns for each one to brainstorm about how you could revise the paragraph.

Noun	Nonrestrictive element that could be added	Punctuation to use

3. Finally, on a separate sheet of paper or the back of this handout, write the revised paragraph with at least three nonrestrictive elements from the table, using appropriate and correct punctuation with commas, parentheses, or dashes.

Volume of Reading Reflection Questions

A Hero's Journey, Grade 6, Module 2

Student Name: ______________________________

Text: ______________________________

Author: ______________________________

Topic: ______________________________

Genre/Type of Book: ______________________________

Share your knowledge about the monomyth genre, the similarities of this genre across cultures, and the role of mythology in cultures.

Informational Text:

1. Wonder: What questions about the hero's journey or mythology did the text inspire?
2. Organize: Summarize a central idea of the text and its supporting details, including details about the hero's journey or mythology.
3. Reveal: Select an important sentence. How does that sentence contribute to the text?
4. Distill: What is the most important insight you gained from this text?
5. Know: How does this text's presentation of information compare and contrast with another text on a similar topic?
6. Vocabulary: Write and define three important vocabulary words that you learned in this text. In what kind of discussions might you use each word (only in discussions of mythology or in other contexts as well)?

Literary Text:

1. Wonder: After reading the first few pages of the text, what inferences can you draw?
2. Organize: Write a short summary of the story including the main character(s), setting, conflict, and resolution.
3. Reveal: What components of the story are consistent with the stages of the hero's journey?
4. Distill: What is a theme of this story? How do particular details convey that theme?
5. Know: What similarities do you see between the characters in this book and the characters you read about in Module 2?
6. Vocabulary: Identify three words that we use today that relate to this text. Explain the connection.

WIT & WISDOM PARENT TIP SHEET

WHAT IS MY SIXTH-GRADE STUDENT LEARNING IN MODULE 2?

Wit & Wisdom is our is our English curriculum. It builds knowledge of key topics in history, science, and literature through the study of excellent texts. By reading and responding to literature and nonfiction texts, we will build knowledge of the following topics:

Module 1: Resilience in the Great Depression

Module 2: A Hero's Journey

Module 3: Narrating the Unknown: Jamestown

Module 4: Courage in Crisis

In this second module, *A Hero's Journey*, we will study what makes a hero. Is it simply courage, or something more? What traits do all of us share with the most famous heroes in literature?

OUR CLASS WILL READ THESE TEXTS:

Myth

- *The Odyssey*, Gillian Cross and Neil Packer
- *Ramayana: Divine Loophole*, Sanjay Patel

Articles

- "The Hero's Journey Outline," Christopher Vogler
- "A Practical Guide to Joseph Campbell's *The Hero with a Thousand Faces*," Christopher Vogler

OUR CLASS WILL WATCH THESE VIDEOS:

- "The Mythology of Star Wars," Bill Moyers and George Lucas
- "Sanjay's Super Team," Sanjay Patel
- "What Makes a Hero?" Matthew Winkler

OUR CLASS WILL ASK THESE QUESTIONS:

- How does *Ramayana: Divine Loophole* exhibit the genre expectations of the monomyth, a story of an extraordinary, but flawed individual who struggles, changes, and impacts the world for good)?
- How does *The Odyssey* exhibit the genre expectations of the monomyth?
- How do translations of *The Odyssey* and *Ramayana* expand our understanding of these texts?
- How does the monomyth genre persist in and influence the stories we tell?
- What is the significance and power of the hero's journey?

QUESTIONS TO ASK AT HOME:

As your sixth-grade student reads, ask:

- *What's happening?*
- *What does a closer look at words and illustrations reveal about this text's deeper meaning?*

BOOKS TO READ AT HOME:

- *Percy Jackson and the Olympians Book 1: The Lightning Thief*, Rick Riordan
- *Life of Pi*, Yann Martel
- *Black Ships Before Troy: The Story of The Iliad*, Rosemary Sutcliff
- *Sita's Ramayana*, Samhita Arni
- *The Hero Schliemann: The Dreamer Who Dug for Troy*, Laura Amy Schlitz
- *The Iliad*, Homer (Retold by Gillian Cross)
- *The Greek Gods*, Bernard Evslin, Dorothy Evslin, and Ned Hoopes
- *The Odyssey*, Homer, Geraldine McCaughrean (Adapter)

IDEAS FOR TALKING ABOUT THE HERO'S JOURNEY:

As you watch movies together, ask:

- *Who was the hero?*
- *What made the hero extraordinary?*
- *What were the hero's flaws?*
- *Describe the hero's struggle.*
- *How did the hero change?*
- *How did the hero impact others or bring about change?*

CREDITS

Great Minds® has made every effort to obtain permission for the reprinting of all copyrighted material. If any owner of copyrighted material is not acknowledged herein, please contact Great Minds® for proper acknowledgment in all future editions and reprints of this module.

- All material from the *Common Core State Standards for English Language Arts & Literacy in History/Social Studies, Science, and Technical Subjects* © Copyright 2010 National Governors Association Center for Best Practices and Council of Chief State School Officers. All rights reserved.
- All images are used under license from Shutterstock.com unless otherwise noted.
- Handout 8A: "The Hero's Journey Outline" and Handout 28A: "A Practical Guide to Joseph Campbell's *The Hero with a Thousand Faces*" from *The Writer's Journey: Mythic Structure for Writers*, Third Edition, by Christopher Vogler. Used with permission from Michael Wiese Productions.
- Handout 29A: *Joseph Campbell and the Power of Myth with Bill Moyers*. Used with permission from The Independent Production Fund / Alvin H. Perlmutter, Inc.
- For updated credit information, please visit http://witeng.link/credits.

ACKNOWLEDGMENTS

Great Minds® Staff

The following writers, editors, reviewers, and support staff contributed to the development of this curriculum.

Ann Brigham, Lauren Chapalee, Sara Clarke, Emily Climer, Lorraine Griffith, Emily Gula, Sarah Henchey, Trish Huerster, Stephanie Kane-Mainier, Lior Klirs, Liz Manolis, Andrea Minich, Lynne Munson, Marya Myers, Rachel Rooney, Aaron Schifrin, Danielle Shylit, Rachel Stack, Sarah Turnage, Michelle Warner, Amy Wierzbicki, Margaret Wilson, and Sarah Woodard.

Colleagues and Contributors

We are grateful for the many educators, writers, and subject-matter experts who made this program possible.

David Abel, Robin Agurkis, Elizabeth Bailey, Julianne Barto, Amy Benjamin, Andrew Biemiller, Charlotte Boucher, Sheila Byrd-Carmichael, Eric Carey, Jessica Carloni, Janine Cody, Rebecca Cohen, Elaine Collins, Tequila Cornelious, Beverly Davis, Matt Davis, Thomas Easterling, Jeanette Edelstein, Kristy Ellis, Moira Clarkin Evans, Charles Fischer, Marty Gephart, Kath Gibbs, Natalie Goldstein, Christina Gonzalez, Mamie Goodson, Nora Graham, Lindsay Griffith, Brenna Haffner, Joanna Hawkins, Elizabeth Haydel, Steve Hettleman, Cara Hoppe, Ashley Hymel, Carol Jago, Jennifer Johnson, Mason Judy, Gail Kearns, Shelly Knupp, Sarah Kushner, Shannon Last, Suzanne Lauchaire, Diana Leddy, David Liben, Farren Liben, Jennifer Marin, Susannah Maynard, Cathy McGath, Emily McKean, Jane Miller, Rebecca Moore, Cathy Newton, Turi Nilsson, Julie Norris, Galemarie Ola, Michelle Palmieri, Meredith Phillips, Shilpa Raman, Tonya Romayne, Emmet Rosenfeld, Jennifer Ruppel, Mike Russoniello, Deborah Samley, Casey Schultz, Renee Simpson, Rebecca Sklepovich, Amelia Swabb, Kim Taylor, Vicki Taylor, Melissa Thomson, Lindsay Tomlinson, Melissa Vail, Keenan Walsh, Julia Wasson, Lynn Welch, Yvonne Guerrero Welch, Emily Whyte, Lynn Woods, and Rachel Zindler.

Early Adopters

The following early adopters provided invaluable insight and guidance for Wit & Wisdom:

- Bourbonnais School District 53 • Bourbonnais, IL
- Coney Island Prep Middle School • Brooklyn, NY
- Gate City Charter School for the Arts • Merrimack, NH
- Hebrew Academy for Special Children • Brooklyn, NY
- Paris Independent Schools • Paris, KY
- Saydel Community School District • Saydel, IA
- Strive Collegiate Academy • Nashville, TN
- Valiente College Preparatory Charter School • South Gate, CA
- Voyageur Academy • Detroit, MI

Design Direction provided by Alton Creative, Inc.

Project management support, production design and copyediting services provided by ScribeConcepts.com

Copyediting services provided by Fine Lines Editing

Product management support provided by Sandhill Consulting